# BATMAN™

## CHARACTER ENCYCLOPEDIA

WRITTEN BY **MATTHEW K. MANNING**

BATMAN CREATED BY **BOB KANE** WITH **BILL FINGER**

# INTRODUCTION

Delve into Batman's world and meet noble Super Heroes, terrifying super-villains, and everyone in between. Discover honorable vigilantes, deadly assassins, heroes gone bad, humans that transform into animals, honest cops, and time-traveling warlords. Who is your favorite? Who wears the best costume? And who has the strangest superpower? Turn the page and find out!

## Contents

Every character in this book has his or her own role to play. Noble heroes use their powers and weapons to fight for justice. The Dark Knight's allies might not have superpowers, but they help out when they can. Neutral characters have been both friend and foe to Batman. Whose side are they on now? And, of course, the rogues—dangerous villains who try to thwart the Dark Knight at every turn. To find a character at superhuman speed, use the index at the back of the book.

# BATMAN

## VITAL STATS

**Real Name:** Bruce Wayne

**Occupation:** Hero, crime fighter

**Height:** 6ft 2in

**Weight:** 210 lbs

**Base:** Gotham City

**Allies:** The Batman Family, the Justice League, Batman, Inc.

**Foes:** Arkham Rogues, Rā's al Ghūl, the Penguin

## POWERS AND ABILITIES

Martial artist; near-genius intellect; skilled detective and gymnast; armored suit and Utility Belt equipped with myriad offensive and defensive devices.

### BEWARE THE BAT

Bruce Wayne adopted the image of a bat in order to strike fear into the hearts of criminals everywhere. This intimidating persona was inspired by Bruce's own childhood encounter with the bats living below Wayne Manor.

**After his parents** were gunned down before his eyes in a senseless act of violence when he was just a young boy, Bruce Wayne dedicated his entire life to protecting the citizens of Gotham City. To that end, he trained his body and mind to near physical perfection and used the Wayne family fortune to create a hi-tech arsenal of unique weapons and vehicles.

*"Father, I shall become a bat."*

Arm gauntlets adorned with scallops that can be used as weapons

Cape helps instill fear in criminals and protects him from gunfire and flames

Bat-symbol has helped make him notorious

Armored Batsuit has reinforced plates at the knees

# BRUCE WAYNE

## VITAL STATS

**Full Name:** Bruce Wayne

**Occupation:** Former head of Wayne Enterprises

**Height:** 6ft 2in

**Weight:** 210 lbs

**Base:** Gotham City

**Allies:** The Batman Family, the Justice League, Batman, Inc.

**Foes:** Arkham Rogues, Rā's al Ghūl, the Penguin

### POWERS AND ABILITIES

Near-genius intellect; incredible social skills; carefully constructed public persona conceals alter ego; enormous resources at his disposal due to contacts at Wayne Enterprises.

### GOTHAM CITY'S FAVORITE SON

One of Gotham City's shining stars, Bruce Wayne is the longtime face of Wayne Enterprises, who often hosts fundraisers for charitable causes. Like his alter ego, Batman, he puts Gotham City's needs before his own.

**Bruce Wayne became** the Batman, fighting to protect Gotham City. However, when he returned to his hometown from traveling and training abroad, he realized the need to create a public persona that would distance him from his nocturnal activities. Bruce became involved in Wayne Enterprises, and built a reputation for himself as a careless bachelor.

*"A better, brighter Gotham is just one dream away."*

Hides in plain sight as public figure

Often dresses formally for social engagements

Can change into Batsuit at lightning speed

Tuxedo from his expensive wardrobe

# ROBIN

## VITAL STATS

**Real Name:** Damian Wayne

**Occupation:** Hero, adventurer

**Height:** 4ft 6in

**Weight:** 84 lbs

**Base:** Gotham City

**Allies:** Batman, the Batman Family, Batman, Inc., Goliath

**Foes:** Rās al Ghūl, the League of Assassins, NoBody

## POWERS AND ABILITIES

Martial artist; skilled detective and gymnast; adept assassin; impressive intellect; as Robin, employs armored suit equipped with a myriad of offensive and defensive devices; protected by a Man-Bat named Goliath; briefly possessed Superman-like powers.

## FATHER AND SON

Batman has mentored several Robins, but none have been his own flesh and blood until Damian. Despite his stubborn personality, Damian holds a special place in the Dark Knight's carefully guarded heart.

**The result of a romance** between Batman and the corrupt Talia al Ghūl, Damian Wayne was grown in a lab. Once he was brought into the world, Talia trained Damian in the deadly ways of the League of Assassins before allowing Batman to meet his son. Damian soon abandoned his mother's violent ways and joined his father as his new partner, Robin.

*"I'm going out, Father. Gotham needs me."*

Trained in martial arts

Utility Belt with smoke pellets and tear gas

Gauntlets similar to Batman's

# GRAYSON

## VITAL STATS

**Full Name:** Richard "Dick" Grayson

**Occupation:** Agent of Spyral, gymnastics teacher

**Height:** 5ft 10in

**Weight:** 175 lbs .

**Base:** Saint Hadrian's Finishing School for Girls, England

**Allies:** Batman, the Batman Family, Helena Bertinelli, Starfire

**Foes:** The Joker, Prankster, Paragon, Tony Zucco

## POWERS AND ABILITIES

Highly skilled acrobat; natural athlete; martial artist; extremely intelligent; trained by Batman; can alter appearance via identity protection implants.

### LIGHTS OUT AT MIDNIGHT

Grayson's adventures with Spyral have put him in direct opposition with the vigilante known as the Midnighter on several occasions. What Midnighter doesn't know is that Grayson is secretly a double agent for Batman.

Equipped with mind-influencing "hypnos"

Favorite weapons are escrima sticks

Belt equipped with variety of hi-tech gadgets

**Soon after young trapeze** artist Dick Grayson watched his parents fall to their deaths, he embarked on a new chapter in his life as Bruce Wayne's adopted son and Batman's partner, Robin. After growing into a Super Hero in his own right—Nightwing—Dick later retired that name after a near-death experience, and went to work at the spy agency Spyral as Agent 37.

*"We've got some lives to save."*

# RED HOOD

## VITAL STATS

**Real Name:** Jason Todd

**Occupation:** Vigilante for hire

**Height:** 6ft

**Weight:** 180 lbs

**Base:** Los Angeles, California

**Allies:** The Outlaws, the Batman Family, Talia al Ghūl, the League of Assassins

**Foes:** The Joker, Rā's al Ghūl, the Untitled

## POWERS AND ABILITIES

Martial artist; skilled detective and gymnast; adept assassin; impressive intellect; trained by Batman; armored suit equipped with offensive and defensive devices.

### OUTLAW BY CHOICE

Jason Todd was given a second lease on life thanks to Talia al Ghūl and the healing properties of the Lazarus Pit. He transitioned from Robin to the Red Hood, and teamed up with other like-minded heroes.

**Jason Todd was discovered** by the Joker at an early age. The Joker had Jason's father arrested and faked his mother's death, maneuvering the boy into position to become Batman's newest Robin. Now in a position to destabilize the Batman family, the Joker killed Jason, not knowing that the young man would later return to life as the Red Hood.

Wears hi-tech protective helmet

Armored suit equipped with myriad devices

Red bat symbol on his costume

*"I don't work for just anyone."*

# RED ROBIN

## VITAL STATS

**Real Name:** Timothy Drake

**Occupation:** Hero

**Height:** 5ft 6in

**Weight:** 131 lbs

**Base:** New York City

**Allies:** The Teen Titans, Batman, the Batman Family, Spoiler

**Foes:** The Penguin, the Mad Hatter, the Joker

## POWERS AND ABILITIES

Martial artist; skilled detective and gymnast; impressive intellect; excellent computer hacker; protective glider suit equipped with myriad offensive and defensive devices; natural born leader.

### A DIFFERENT DRUMMER
As the third person to bear the name Robin, Tim Drake decided to set himself apart from the crowd and opted for the title Red Robin instead. After serving as Batman's partner for a time, he soon formed his own team, the Teen Titans.

**A gifted gymnast** and scholar, high school student Tim Drake wanted nothing more than to fight crime with the Dark Knight. To that end, he used his computer hacking skills to steal the Penguin's fortune. The Penguin retaliated against Tim's family, forcing Batman to place them in protective custody. Tim stayed in Gotham City and became Batman's partner, Red Robin.

*"I want to apply for the job."*

Red Robin's role as the leader of the Teen Titans has placed him in many life-and-death situations, including facing the villain known as Grymm.

# BATGIRL

## VITAL STATS

**Real Name:** Barbara Gordon
**Occupation:** Hero, graduate student
**Height:** 5ft 11in
**Weight:** 135 lbs
**Base:** Burnside, Gotham City
**Allies:** The Birds of Prey, the Batman Family, James Gordon
**Foes:** The Joker, James Gordon, Jr., Knightfall, Velvet Tiger

## POWERS AND ABILITIES

Expert martial artist and gymnast; intelligent and excellent strategist; natural leader; athletic and agile; uses compactible Batcycle; trained by Batman.

## PACKING A PUNCH

Batgirl has worn several costumes over the years. She adopted her second official uniform when returning to crime fighting after a temporary hiatus. This costume was highly armored and utilized all of Batman's technology.

**The daughter of** police commissioner James Gordon, Barbara Gordon idolized Batman from a young age. One day, at police headquarters, Barbara adopted a police-developed Batsuit to protect her brother from an escaping criminal. After Batman complimented her on her actions, she realized her true calling and donned a mask and cape as Batgirl.

*"Shut up and hug, tough girl."*

Can remember with expert precision

Designed her own protective costume

Smartphone to use social media to her advantage

Fully stocked Utility Belt

# BATWOMAN

## VITAL STATS

**Real Name:** Katherine (Kate) Kane

**Occupation:** Hero, socialite

**Height:** 5ft 11in

**Weight:** 141 lbs

**Base:** Gotham City

**Allies:** Hawkfire, Batman, the Batman Family, the Unknowns

**Foes:** Nocturna, Ceto, Wolf Spider, Mr. Bones

## POWERS AND ABILITIES

Martial artist; skilled detective and gymnast; highly trained soldier; studied under elite operatives known as the Murder of Crows.

## ESTRANGED FAMILY

Unlike Batgirl or Robin, Batwoman doesn't operate with Batman's seal of approval. The two clashed when Batwoman's then employers, the Department of Extranormal Operations (D.E.O.), ordered her to find out the Dark Knight's secret identity.

**Bruce Wayne's cousin** Kate Kane lived a happy life, until her mother was killed. Kate was raised by her father, Colonel Jacob Kane, whose military connections enabled her to train with some of the world's finest fighters. Kate struggled to find her direction in life until an encounter with Batman inspired her to fight crime in her own unique style as Batwoman.

*"I will soldier on."*

Wears long-haired wig to mask identity

Arm gauntlets can fire grappling line

Protective suit equipped with myriad devices

Utility Belt houses array of useful tools

# SPOILER

## VITAL STATS

**Real Name:** Stephanie Brown

**Occupation:** Hero, student

**Height:** 5ft 5in

**Weight:** 110 lbs

**Base:** Gotham City

**Allies:** Red Robin, Bluebird, Catwoman, Batman

**Foes:** Cluemaster, Hush, Lincoln March

## POWERS AND ABILITIES

Skilled motorcyclist; smart mind and able to think quickly on her feet; skilled gymnast and fighter; protective suit equipped with offensive and defensive devices.

### SPOILER ALERT

As a kid, Stephanie Brown liked to push the envelope and attempt extremely difficult bike stunts. So it wasn't much different for her to risk life and limb when she adopted the vigilante role of the Spoiler.

**Stephanie Brown's life** changed drastically when she interrupted her father's "puzzle night" with his friends, only to learn he was the super-villain known as Cluemaster. On the run from her parents, Stephanie soon discovered that her father was behind a scheme to destroy Batman. She fought against him, and adopted the identity of the costumed Super Hero called the Spoiler.

*"No, Dad. You're done. I'm just getting started."*

After the Cluemaster was defeated, Spoiler still wanted to pursue a Super Hero lifestyle, and pleaded with Catwoman to train her.

# AZRAEL

## VITAL STATS

**Real Name:** Michael Washington Lane

**Occupation:** Hero

**Height:** 6ft 2in

**Weight:** 209 lbs

**Base:** Gotham City

**Allies:** Batman, the Batman Family, the Order of Purity, Batman, Inc.

**Foes:** Rā's al Ghūl, Leviathan, Dr. Hurt

## POWERS AND ABILITIES

Advanced military and police training; wears protective mystical armor; excellent hand-to-hand combatant; skilled swordsman; wields the magical Sword of Sin and Sword of Salvation.

### LIFE OF SORROW

Azrael wears the Suit of Sorrows, an ancient suit of armor that Batman once wore. Azrael was once deputized into Batman, Inc., where he lent Batman his armor to wear in battle against the forces of the terrorist agency Leviathan.

**Michael Lane was a former** college athlete and a Marine who joined the Gotham City Police Department, but was later dismissed. However, Lane joined a secret program between the military and the G.C.P.D. to create a Batman replacement. Later, Lane was approached by a covert organization called the Order of Purity, to be their vigilante, Azrael.

Suit of Sorrows armor is cursed

Mystical Sword of Salvation brings the truth to light

Costume reflects extreme religious mindset

*"I am God's vengeance... his angel of death."*

# ALFRED PENNYWORTH

**ALLY**

## VITAL STATS

**Full Name:** Alfred Pennyworth

**Occupation:** Bruce Wayne's butler

**Height:** 6ft

**Weight:** 160 lbs

**Base:** Gotham City

**Allies:** Batman, the Batman Family, Julia Pennyworth

**Foes:** Arkham Rogues, Hush

## POWERS AND ABILITIES

Skilled surgeon; military combat training; expert actor; computer expert; valued confidant.

### A STEADY HAND

There is far more to Alfred's responsibilities than cooking and cleaning for billionaire Bruce Wayne. With full knowledge of Batman's identity, Alfred has saved Bruce's life on many occasions, putting his surgery skills to good use.

**As loyal butler** to Thomas and Martha Wayne, Alfred Pennyworth did his best to raise their son Bruce after their tragic deaths. Alfred stood by his young master's side, helping him build his career as Batman. While he often wishes Bruce would retire from crime fighting, Alfred nevertheless feels honored to play a role in Batman's mission.

*"...I'll always be there to patch you up."*

Dubbed Penny-One during radio transmissions, Alfred often works at the Batcomputer, feeding Batman information when he is in the field.

# JULIA PENNYWORTH

ALLY

## VITAL STATS

**Full Name:** Julia Pennyworth

**Occupation:** Batman task force strategist, former SRR agent

**Height:** 5ft 8in

**Weight:** 129 lbs

**Base:** Gotham City

**Allies:** Batman, James Gordon, Alfred Pennyworth, G.C.P.D.

**Foes:** Shen Fang, Hush, the Joker

## POWERS AND ABILITIES

Highly trained special agent; expert marksman; computer expert; efficient spy and strategist; has access to Batman's crime files and technology.

### IN FOR A PENNY...

Julia began helping Batman from the Batcave as Penny-Two after Alfred was injured by Hush. After Batman's assumed "death," she began working as part of the G.C.P.D.'s Batman task force as Julia Perry.

**An agent for the** British Special Reconnaissance Regiment, Julia Pennyworth first crossed paths with Batman in Hong Kong when he was investigating Carmine Falcone and Shen Fang. Fang stabbed Julia, badly injuring her. Learning that Julia was Alfred's daughter, Batman brought her to Wayne Manor, where she discovered his double life and reconciled with her father, Alfred.

*"Turn on the lights down here and show Jim his Batmobile."*

It didn't take Julia long to figure out the Batcomputer. She usually assists from the Batcave, but has occasionally ventured out into the field.

# BATWING

HERO

## VITAL STATS

**Real Name:** Lucas "Luke" Fox

**Occupation:** Hero, mixed martial arts fighter

**Height:** 5ft 9in

**Weight:** 170 lbs

**Base:** Gotham City

**Allies:** Batman, Lucius Fox, the Batman Family, Batman, Inc.

**Foes:** Lady Vic, Ratcatcher, Charlie Caligula, Menace

## POWERS AND ABILITIES

Talented martial arts fighter; brilliant designer and engineer; quick witted; suit allows for hi-tech weaponry and defense systems, flight and limited invisibility; near unlimited access to Wayne Enterprises technology.

## WINGING IT

One of Batwing's first missions had him partner with Batman to face the Marabunta, an ant-like colony of villains employed by the criminal Charlie Caligula. Batwing defeated the organization's sects in Africa and Gotham City.

**When Batman formed** his crime-fighting organization, Batman, Inc., he hand-picked worthy individuals to join the team. He chose Luke, son of his longtime friend—and Wayne Enterprises CEO—Lucius Fox, to become the armored hero Batwing. While his secret Batwing career has caused family problems for Luke, he has embraced life as a Super Hero.

*"It's all part of my job."*

Bat-symbol can project bursts of brilliant light

Helmet equipped with "Detective Vision"

Built-in Utility Belt to store small devices

Bulletproof armor protects and seals underwater

Gauntlets can fire grappling line

# BLUEBIRD

## VITAL STATS

**Real Name:** Harper Row
**Occupation:** Hero, student
**Height:** 5ft 5in
**Weight:** 112 lbs
**Base:** Gotham City
**Allies:** Batman, Red Robin, the Batman Family, Cullen Row
**Foes:** The Mad Hatter, the Joker, Lincoln March

## POWERS AND ABILITIES

Electronics expert; great at fixing things; protective suit equipped with myriad offensive and defensive devices; uses taser rifle.

### NO KILLING A MOCKINGBIRD

After repeatedly proving her worth to Batman, Harper Row began to fight by Red Robin's side. She eventually developed her own identity as Bluebird to battle the Mad Hatter, and became Batman's newest ally.

**The daughter of** a deadbeat father, Harper Row was forced to take on responsibilities at an early age and practically raised her brother Cullen. As a teenager with a talent for electronics, she and her brother were rescued by the Batman one night. Inspired by the hero, Harper hacked into his network and helped in a battle with Tiger Shark.

*"Batman doesn't get to die."*

Cut hair to take a stand against brother's bullies

Suit has anti-nanotechnology barrier

Belt contains smoke capsules and Batarangs

# TALON

## VITAL STATS

**Real Name:** Calvin Rose
**Occupation:** Hero
**Height:** 5ft 10in
**Weight:** 174 lbs
**Base:** Gotham City
**Allies:** Batman, Batman, Inc., Strix, Casey Washington
**Foes:** The Court of Owls, Bane, Lord Death Man, Sebastian Clark

### POWERS AND ABILITIES

Expert escape artist; adept in several fighting styles and knife-throwing; knowledge of electronics, specifically security systems; expert assassin, despite now practicing non-lethal crime fighting.

## OWL VS. BAT

At first Batman did not approve of Talon's crusade against the Court of Owls, fearing innocent lives may be in jeopardy. However, he soon saw Talon's true heroism, and recruited him into Batman, Inc.

**At eight years old,** Calvin Rose was locked and abandoned in a dog kennel by his father. After three nights, he managed to break out, and was discovered by an escape artist who worked at Haly's Circus. Calvin trained and became the man's successor, and was then recruited by the Court of Owls as a Talon assassin. But he escaped that world too, in favor of the life of a hero.

Armor gifted to him by the Court of Owls

Belt equipped with items like lock picks

Gauntlets can fire grappling line and darts

*"I'm never running away again."*

# HAWKFIRE

## VITAL STATS

**Real Name:** Bette Kane

**Occupation:** Student, crime fighter

**Height:** 5ft 6in

**Weight:** 120 lbs

**Base:** Gotham City

**Allies:** Batwoman, Jacob Kane

**Foes:** The Hook, Mr. Freeze, Bane

## POWERS AND ABILITIES

Martial artist; skilled detective and gymnast; trained by Batwoman and Jacob Kane; studied under elite operatives known as the Murder of Crows; wing pack allows her to fly.

### A DYNAMIC DUO?

Hawkfire is the optimistic Robin to Batwoman's more practical Batman. Full of life and hope, with more than a little skill of her own, Hawkfire has proven herself as a true crime fighter, despite Batwoman's concerns.

**Bette Kane's desire** to be a Super Hero was long held. Originally operating as the crime-fighting heroine Flamebird, Bette learned that her cousin Kate Kane was moonlighting as Batwoman. Kate took her cousin under her wing and Bette adopted the identity of Hawkfire. Operating as Batwoman's sometime partner, Bette is helped out by her uncle, Jacob Kane.

*"You don't know how badly I need this..."*

Lenses in mask similar to Batwoman's

Gauntlets equipped with flamethrowers

Costume possibly inspired by Nightwing's

Protective suit fitted with functioning wings

# CATWOMAN

## VITAL STATS

**Real Name:** Selina Kyle

**Occupation:** Crime boss and thief, sometime hero, owner of Egyptian Casino

**Height:** 5ft 7in

**Weight:** 128 lbs

**Base:** Gotham City

**Allies:** Killer Croc, the Justice League of America, Batman, Inc., Alice Tesla

**Foes:** The Joker's Daughter, Bone, Black Mask

## POWERS AND ABILITIES

Master cat burglar; expert fighter; accomplished gymnast. Weapons include cat-o-nine-tails whip and gloves with diamond-tipped claws.

## GIVING BACK

Selina Kyle learned to steal at an early age while living at an orphanage. She became an expert cat burglar, but retains a strict moral code that compels her to protect the underprivileged, often joining forces with Batman.

**Selina Kyle's father** is the notorious former Gotham City crime boss, Rex "the Lion" Calabrese. She unknowingly began to follow in his footsteps after being thrown from a rooftop when investigating her own past. She crafted a Catwoman costume out of the awning that saved her life, later rising up the ranks of the underworld to become a crime boss herself.

*"In case you hadn't noticed, I don't fight crime, I am crime."*

Many gadgets devised by Alice Tesla

Belt doubles as a whip

Bodysuit allows freedom of movement

# THE BIRDS OF PREY

## VITAL STATS

**Team Name:** The Birds of Prey
**Base:** Gotham City
**Allies:** Batman, the Batman Family, Mother Eve
**Foes:** The Penguin, Mr. Freeze, Rā's al Ghūl

**Members:** Batgirl, Black Canary, Katana, Strix, Condor, Poison Ivy (traitor), Starling (traitor)

### ENEMIES AND FRENEMIES
The Birds of Prey fought several villains including Mr. Freeze, Rā's al Ghūl, and even former teammate, Poison Ivy. Team members often had trouble seeing eye to eye, eventually leading to the team's disbandment.

**After serving time** as an agent with the Team 7 government strike force, Canary (Dinah Lance) went solo. She changed her name to Black Canary and gained employment at the Iceberg Casino to break up a deal between the Penguin and terrorist organization Basilisk. During this operation she met Starling and Batgirl, who would later join forces with her as the Birds of Prey.

*"...Nobody on this team has a squeaky-clean soul."*

Strix was brought onto the team by Batgirl

Black Canary relished serving on a new team

Batgirl took over as leader after Black Canary

Batgirl eventually disbanded the Birds

# BLACK CANARY

## VITAL STATS

**Real Name:** Dinah Drake Lance

**Occupation:** Hero, singer

**Height:** 5ft 4in

**Weight:** 115 lbs

**Base:** Mobile

**Allies:** Batgirl, the Birds of Prey, Batman

**Foes:** Basilisk, Rā's al Ghūl, the Penguin

## POWERS AND ABILITIES

Expert martial artist with advanced military training; intelligent and an excellent strategist; natural leader; Canary Cry strong enough to shatter walls; well connected in the intelligence and Super Hero worlds.

## A LIFE LESS ORDINARY

Black Canary lives a life of endless changes. After a long stint with the crime fighters called the Birds of Prey, she decided to go solo, and found herself the lead singer of her own band, aptly named Black Canary.

**Abandoned as a child,** Dinah Drake found a home at a dojo (martial arts school) in Gotham City, where she trained until she was discovered by the US government. She joined special ops group Team 7, where she took part in genetic testing and discovered her Canary Cry—the ability to deliver an ultrasonic scream. Dinah later went freelance as Super Hero Black Canary.

Uses powerful voice to headline band

Recently started wearing punk rock attire

Extremely athletic and agile

> *"We've got a big day tomorrow. Rock 'n' roll."*

# LADY BLACKHAWK

HERO

## VITAL STATS

**Real Name:** Zinda Blake

**Occupation:** Hero, pilot

**Height:** 5ft 7in

**Weight:** 117 lbs

**Base:** Mobile

**Allies:** The Birds of Prey, Blackhawks

**Foes:** The Penguin, Killer Shark

## POWERS AND ABILITIES

Expert pilot, who can handle any kind of aircraft with ease; adept hand-to-hand combatant; proficient marksman.

## BLACKHAWK DOWN

Zinda Blake has never been one to back down from a challenge, and more often than not can be found brawling in whatever bar she's chosen to drink in on any particular night. Nevertheless, she became a valued ally to the Birds of Prey.

Sign up at recruitment center near you.

**Lady Blackhawk was a** member of the Blackhawks, a secretive squadron of ace pilots who fought during World War II. After traveling through time, Lady Blackhawk temporarily served as a pilot for the Birds of Prey. More unruly than her fellow Super Heroes, Lady Blackhawk has nevertheless proven that she can hold her own in nearly any fight.

*"Gonna be one beautiful flight."*

Pilot jacket is flexible to allow ease of movement

Old fashioned costume shows difficulty adjusting to modern times

Wears traditional Blackhawk symbol

# STRIX

## VITAL STATS

**Real Name:** Mary Turner

**Occupation:** Hero, former assassin

**Height:** 5ft 7in

**Weight:** 120 lbs

**Base:** Gotham City

**Allies:** Batgirl, the Birds of Prey, Talon, the Secret Six

**Foes:** The Court of Owls, Mr. Freeze, Rās al Ghūl

## POWERS AND ABILITIES

Expert assassin and fighter trained by the Court of Owls; natural acrobat; genius IQ; extremely observant; possesses healing factor and can "die" and be brought to life again.

## ROUGH START

After encountering Batgirl during a battle against the Court of Owls, Strix was recruited to join the Birds of Prey. There was some friction between the teammates at first, but she soon became a trusted member of their entourage.

**During an attack** on the United States by Japan in 1944, a girl named Mary was badly scarred, losing her tongue as well as her family. She found work at Haly's Circus, but despite being a talented aerialist, she stayed behind the scenes as her face frightened audiences. She was recruited by the Court of Owls, but broke free of their influence thanks to Batgirl.

*"Hrrrnnn!"*

Altered costume slightly to fool the Court of Owls

Does not speak, just grunts

Clawed fingertips on gloves

CONDOR

## VITAL STATS

**Real Name:**
Benjamin Reyes
**Occupation:** Hero,
former terrorist agent
**Height:** 6ft
**Weight:** 199 lbs
**Base:** Gotham City
**Allies:** The Birds of Prey,
Mother Eve
**Foes:** Strike Force Basilisk,
Regulus

### POWERS AND ABILITIES
Telekinetic abilities can
produce energy blasts
or shields; flight; armored
battle suit; expert at
various languages.

### FLIGHT OF THE CONDOR
Condor turned his criminal life around to
become the sole male member of the Birds
of Prey. He encountered the Birds while
in Japan, and grew quite fond of Black
Canary, hoping for a romance with her.

Mind can
produce energy
blasts or shields

Flight powered
by telekinetic
abilities

**Ben Reyes lost his** security job due to
crippling headaches. He couldn't bear
the pain, but he was soon taken in
by Tsiklon, a member of the terrorist
organization Basilisk. Ben realized
his pains were just his growing
powers. He learned later how
corrupt his Basilisk saviors were
and quit their team, changing his
codename from Poltergeist to Condor.

*"I'm good at catching bullets."*

Armored battle suit
built by a Basilisk
prisoner that
Condor rescued

## VITAL STATS

**Team Name:** Batman, Inc.

**Base:** Gotham City and various countries around the globe

**Allies:** Batman, the Batman Family, Batwoman, Wayne Enterprises

**Foes:** Talia al Ghūl, Scorpiana, Heretic

**Members:** Batman, Robin, Red Robin, Catwoman, Dick Grayson, Batgirl, Batwing, Batwing (Luke Fox), Nightrunner, Batman Japan, Wingman, the Knight (Cyril Sheldrake) (deceased), the Knight (formerly the Squire), El Gaucho, Man-of-Bats, Hood, Raven Red, Dark Ranger, Black Bat, Metamorpho, Katana, Halo, Looker, Freight Train, the Huntress, Batman of Moscow (deceased)

### INCORPORATING THE WORLD

Batman, Incorporated succeeded in establishing officially licensed Batmen around the world, protecting countries as diverse as France, Japan, and Russia. The team even found an unofficial mascot in the form of Bat-Cow.

**After a brush with death**, Batman learned of a new threat to the world in the secret society called Leviathan. Using funding from Wayne Enterprises, Bruce Wayne publicly launched Batman, Incorporated, a mission to place a "Batman" in various cities around the globe. While it cost him the lives of a few members, Batman, Inc. was a success that ended Leviathan's threat.

Batman led Batman, Inc., even after it was banned from activity in Gotham City

The Squire graduated to become the Knight after the death of her partner

*"Ladies and gentlemen. I give you Batman, Incorporated!"*

# EL GAUCHO

## VITAL STATS

**Real Name:** Santiago Vargas

**Occupation:** Hero, wealthy socialite

**Height:** 6ft 1in

**Weight:** 215 lbs

**Base:** Buenos Aires, Argentina

**Allies:** Batman, Batman, Inc., the Club of Heroes

**Foes:** The Club of Villains, Leviathan, Dr. Hurt, Scorpiana, El Sombrero

## POWERS AND ABILITIES

Highly trained hand-to-hand combatant; usually drives motorcycle during missions; intelligent and extremely wealthy.

### THE MARK OF GAUCHO

El Gaucho and Batman once teamed up to track down Dr. Dedalus, a Spyral agent. The Dark Knight's respect for El Gaucho is perhaps due to him seeing a bit of his childhood hero, Zorro, in the crime fighter.

**In the early days** of Batman's career, billionaire John Mayhew recruited him to be part of the Club of Heroes alongside other international crime fighters. While Batman didn't find the Club to his liking, he later enlisted many of its members into his own team, Batman, Inc., including El Gaucho, who represented his native country, Argentina.

*"...the tango of death is over!"*

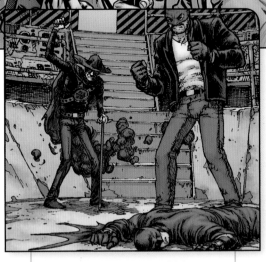

El Gaucho was secretly Agent 33 for Spyral. However, he turned on his boss, Dr. Dedalus, and saved Batman's life.

# THE KNIGHT

## VITAL STATS

**Real Name:** Cyril Sheldrake
**Occupation:** Hero
**Height:** 6ft 2in
**Weight:** 209 lbs
**Base:** Wordenshire, England
**Allies:** The Squire, the Knight I, Batman, Batman, Inc., the Club of Heroes
**Foes:** Springheeled Jack, Morris Men, Leviathan, Heretic

## POWERS AND ABILITIES

Expert martial artist; skilled detective and gymnast; impressive intellect; armored suit equipped with myriad devices; natural born leader; vast supply of vehicles and weapons.

### KNIGHT IN WAITING

The Knight and his partner, the Squire, were fairly inseparable, often spending time at their favorite pub, the Time in a Bottle. When the Knight was killed, the Squire took his place after mourning her old friend.

**Cyril Sheldrake used to** be known as the Squire—a loyal sidekick to his father Percy, the original Knight. The pair were the so-called Batman and Robin of England. As the Squire, he joined the Club of Heroes with his father. Later graduating to the position of the Knight, Cyril would become a member of Batman, Inc., and perish in a deadly battle with the Heretic.

*"Don't let them win, Beryl..."*

Being the Knight was a family tradition, which Cyril took on gladly. He stepped into his father's large shoes, and made the role of the Knight his own.

# THE SQUIRE

## VITAL STATS

**Real Name:** Beryl Hutchinson
**Occupation:** Hero
**Height:** 5ft 5in
**Weight:** 108 lbs
**Base:** Wordenshire, England
**Allies:** The Knight II, Batman, Inc., Dark Ranger II, Red Robin
**Foes:** Springheeled Jack, Morris Men, Leviathan, Heretic

## POWERS AND ABILITIES

Expert martial artist; skilled detective and gymnast; impressive intellect; armored suit equipped with myriad offensive and defensive devices; natural born leader; vast supply of vehicles and weapons.

## TRAVELING SQUIRE

Though based in England, the Squire had been to Gotham City several times, as the Squire, then as the Knight. An adept crime fighter, she is even more determined now that her mentor has died.

**After discovering the secret** identity of the Knight, Beryl Hutchinson helped the hero against his foe, Springheeled Jack, and was sworn in as the Knight's Squire. As a member of Batman, Inc., the Squire helped recruit her ally and future love interest, Dark Ranger, before taking the mantle of the Knight following her partner's death.

*"I wasn't taking this seriously enough but I am now."*

After her mentor was killed, the Squire stepped up to be the third hero to be known as the Knight, lashing out at the forces of Leviathan.

# MAN-OF-BATS

## VITAL STATS

**Real Name:** Dr. William Great Eagle
**Occupation:** Hero, doctor
**Height:** 6ft 1in
**Weight:** 224 lbs
**Base:** South Dakota
**Allies:** Raven Red, Batman, Inc., the Club of Heroes
**Foes:** The Club of Villains, Leviathan, Dr. Hurt

## POWERS AND ABILITIES

Highly trained hand-to-hand combatant; intelligent and trained as a medical doctor; expert archer and horseback rider; efficient with many traditional Native American weapons; runs imitation Batcave/tourist attraction.

### RIDING INTO THE SUNSET
Both Man-of-Bats and his sidekick and son, Raven Red, have teamed with Batman. Batman visited their small town when Leviathan targeted Man-of-Bats due to his association with the Dark Knight.

**One of the many** Batman-inspired crime fighters to join the Club of Heroes, Man-of-Bats fights for justice on a Native American reservation in South Dakota. While he has modeled himself after the Dark Knight, Man-of-Bats prefers to employ traditional Native American weapons and dress, displaying them alongside his trophies in his own "Bat's Cave."

*"Better send a Bat-Signal."*

Man-of-Bats's actions have been an issue for law enforcement as he acts fast in emergencies, but doesn't always consider the consequences.

# RAVEN RED

## VITAL STATS

**Real Name:** Charles Great Eagle

**Occupation:** Hero

**Height:** 5ft 9in

**Weight:** 168 lbs

**Base:** South Dakota

**Allies:** Man-of-Bats, Batman, Inc., the Club of Heroes

**Foes:** The Club of Villains, Leviathan, Dr. Hurt

## POWERS AND ABILITIES

Highly trained hand-to-hand combatant; highly intelligent; expert archer, horseback rider and efficient with traditional Native American weapons; helps run imitation Batcave/tourist attraction; wears bullet-repelling "ghost shirt."

### LITTLE BIG MAN

Raven Red used to be called Little Raven, a name he grew out of during his crime-fighting career. He has yet to truly emerge from his father's shadow, however, and remains Man-of-Bats's steadfast partner.

**The son of Man-of-Bats**, Raven Red was disappointed in his father for leaving San Francisco after Raven's mother died. He soon began to recognize the nobility in his father's mission to protect their ancestral home. Even so, he has felt that he was personally destined for something bigger, like a membership in the Teen Titans.

*"We can handle this our way, like we always do."*

Raven Red wears the "Ghost Shirt." His father once sat outside a museum for days in order to reclaim the shirt for his Bat's Cave museum.

# BATMAN JAPAN

## VITAL STATS

**Real Name:** Jiro Osamu

**Occupation:** Hero

**Height:** 5ft 10in

**Weight:** 173 lbs

**Base:** Tokyo, Japan

**Allies:** Mr. Unknown, Batman, Inc., Lolita Canary

**Foes:** Lord Death Man, Leviathan, Doubleface, Lady Tiger Fist, Dr. Inside-Out

## POWERS AND ABILITIES

Highly skilled martial artist and acrobat; trained by the original Mr. Unknown; wears protective costume equipped with hi-tech gadgets; employs cutting edge weapons and vehicles supplied by Batman, Inc.

### LIFE AFTER DEATH

To become Batman Japan, Jiro faked his death as the hero Mr. Unknown. It was his way of starting fresh and beginning his own legacy. He later set up his own base, a hideout modeled after that of his hero and ally, Batman.

**Jiro Osamu was the assistant** to the Japanese hero Mr. Unknown, his "body double" of sorts. While Mr. Unknown was the brains of the operation, Jiro did the physical part: patrols, stakeouts, and street fighting. When Mr. Unknown was killed by Lord Death Man, Jiro stepped up as the new Mr. Unknown. He was soon asked to join Batman, Inc. as Batman Japan.

*"Guns are for cowards."*

Batman Japan's costumes have changed frequently over the years, He employs his current look when teaming up with his girlfriend, Lolita Canary.

# NIGHTRUNNER

## VITAL STATS

**Real Name:** Bilal Asselah
**Occupation:** Hero
**Height:** 5ft 10in
**Weight:** 167 lbs
**Base:** Paris, France
**Allies:** Batman, Inc., Batman, Dick Grayson
**Foes:** Leviathan, La Muerte en Vida, the Man Who Laughs

### POWERS AND ABILITIES

Expert at parkour free-running; highly acrobatic; trained in hand-to-hand combat by Dick Grayson; extremely athletic and fast; access to Batman, Inc. equipment and funds; Utility Belt includes a grapnel gun.

### RUNNING MAN

When Batman and Dick Grayson helped curb riots in Paris caused by bizarre assassinations, Nightrunner caught their eye. He was soon deputized as a Batman, Inc. member, and later replaced the retired Musketeer as the Batman of France.

**A Sunni Muslim born** in the outskirts of Paris, France, Bilal Asselah lost a friend during a riot in his neighborhood, experiencing firsthand the horror of violence. Out of frustration, he started running over the rooftops. Soon, people began to notice his dynamic runs. With the makings of a local hero, he adopted the name Nightrunner and sought to curb the violence of his city.

*"Well, I guess if we've already got the suit..."*

Adopted mask when he started getting noticed

Altered shirt as a nod to Batman

Toned physique from countless rooftop runs

Utility Belt stocked with helpful gadgets

# BLACK BAT

## VITAL STATS

**Real Name:** Cassandra Cain

**Occupation:** Hero

**Height:** 5ft 5in

**Weight:** 110 lbs

**Base:** Gotham City

**Allies:** Batman, Batman, Inc., Red Robin

**Foes:** David Cain, Leviathan, Lady Shiva

## POWERS AND ABILITIES

One of the best martial artists in the world; able to read the body language of others and predict their next move; incredibly athletic with quick reflexes; trained by an expert assassin; Utility Belt full of useful devices; access to Batman, Inc. equipment.

### SILENT PREDATOR

Black Bat is a natural fighter whose abilities were magnified when her father, David Cain, refused to teach her how to talk. Instead, she learned to communicate through body language and violence.

**The daughter of assassin** David Cain and Lady Shiva, Cassandra Cain was born with a natural aptitude toward athletics and the fighting arts. Raised by her father, Cassandra perfected his assassin skills at an early age, and once even killed for him. Realizing this was wrong, Cassandra fled from her father and wound up in Gotham City, later adopting the identity of Black Bat.

*"I think I've always liked it in Gotham."*

Joining Batman's allies proved beneficial for Cassandra. She learned to speak, and also became a valued member of Batman, Inc.

# THE HOOD

## VITAL STATS

**Real Name:** George Cross
**Occupation:** Hero, spy
**Height:** 5ft 10in
**Weight:** 172 lbs
**Base:** London, England
**Allies:** Batman, Batman, Inc., Spyral, T.H.E.Y.
**Foes:** Leviathan, Dr. Dedalus

## POWERS AND ABILITIES

Highly trained hand-to-hand combatant and martial artist; athletic and agile; expert spy; access to Batman, Inc. equipment as well as his own Hood-themed jet; fully stocked Utility Belt; excellent detective skills.

### PICK A SIDE

The Hood kept his involvement in the clandestine organization known as Spyral a secret from his Batman, Inc. cohorts. However, the Hood was fighting on Batman's side all along, especially when it came to his opposition of Leviathan.

Styles himself after Robin Hood

Costume based on medieval knight armor

Cross logo hints at his real name

**Inspired by Robin Hood,** George Cross takes money from criminals and gives it to the poor. When Batman first met the Hood in London, he was impressed, and he thought of the British hero when he later formed Batman, Inc. The Hood accepted the Dark Knight's offer to join the organization, and used the opportunity to become a triple agent, working for England's Super Secret Service (T.H.E.Y.) and Spyral.

*"World's greatest assassins... meet Batman's front line."*

# DARK RANGER

## VITAL STATS

**Real Name:** Johnny Riley
**Occupation:** Hero
**Height:** 5ft 10in
**Weight:** 181 lbs
**Base:** Melbourne, Australia
**Allies:** Batman, Inc.,
Dark Ranger I, Batman,
the Squire
**Foes:** Leviathan,
La Muerte en Vida

## POWERS AND ABILITIES

Utilizes armored suit inherited from the original Dark Ranger; jet pack enables flight; carries pistol that fires electro-stun blasts; uniform has pouches that contain various hi-tech gadgets and weapons.

### PEP TALK

Dark Ranger was sworn into Batman, Inc. by Batman himself. Always a bit cynical, Riley was convinced to give Batman, Inc. a try by the Squire, and the two even became romantically involved.

**Johnny Riley used to** be the Super Hero sidekick to the Ranger—the Australian version of Batman. As the years passed, the Ranger became the Dark Ranger and Scout gave up the heroic life. However, when the Dark Ranger was murdered, Riley donned his mentor's suit and took up the mantle of the Dark Ranger. He was soon recruited into Batman, Inc.

*"You gotta let me try out one of your batarangs."*

The original Ranger traded in a boy scout look for riot gear. The second Dark Ranger, Johnny Riley, follows suit, carrying an array of non-lethal weapons.

# BAT-MITE

## VITAL STATS

**Real Name:** Unknown

**Occupation:** Other-dimensional imp, self-proclaimed hero

**Height:** 2ft 11in

**Weight:** 47 lbs

**Base:** Gotham City

**Allies:** Batman, the Batman Family, Booster Gold

**Foes:** Gridlock, Dr. Trauma

## POWERS AND ABILITIES

Flight; teleportation; can change clothing or appearance of others; wears Utility Belt filled with gadgets, including a bat-shaped cellphone, shield, and a laser.

### THE DARK-MITE RETURNS

After escaping death by drowning at the hands of Dr. Trauma's lackeys, Bat-Mite returned to the villain's hideout. He prevented Trauma from switching her mind with that of the hero Hawkman.

**More of a nuisance than** a threat or an ally, Bat-Mite has labeled himself Batman's number one fan. In fact, in his warped mind, he is the hero and Batman is merely his sidekick. Bat-Mite comes from another dimension and he has some magical powers, but he treats crime fighting like a game, and often prevents Batman from stopping villains in an efficient fashion.

*"All in a day's work for a champion of justice."*

Batman was not happy when the imp hijacked the Batmobile and sped it over a ravine. Yet he still stopped the criminals Bat-Mite was pursuing.

# TITUS

## VITAL STATS

**Full Name:** Titus

**Occupation:**
Robin's pet

**Height:** 3ft 1in

**Weight:** 140 lbs

**Base:** Gotham City

**Allies:** Robin, the Batman
Family, Alfred Pennyworth

**Foes:** Apokolips soldiers,
Kalibak

## POWERS AND ABILITIES

Purebred Great Dane;
excellent sense of smell
and hearing; fiercely loyal
to the Batman Family;
brave and known to
rush head first into
battle; fit and trim.

### HOUND OF THE APOKOLIPS

Titus tagged along to Apokolips when
Batman, Red Robin, Nightwing, Batgirl,
and Red Hood invaded the planet to
retrieve the temporarily dead body of
Robin. Titus held his own, taking out
vicious attack dogs.

**Bruce Wayne noticed** that his son
Damian was having a hard time
transitioning into the life of a Super
Hero, so he bought a Great Dane to
serve as the boy's pet. When Damian
eventually took to the animal, he
named it Titus and the dog has been
his loyal friend ever since. Damian
then adopted more animals, including
a cat named Alfred.

*"Rrarf."*

Acute sense
of hearing
and smell

Named after
character from
Shakespeare

In excellent
physical
condition

# BAT-COW

## VITAL STATS

**Full Name:** Bat-Cow

**Occupation:** Robin's pet

**Height:** 5ft

**Weight:** 1,252 lbs

**Base:** Gotham City

**Allies:** Robin, Alfred Pennyworth, the Batman Family

**Foes:** Meat eaters

### POWERS AND ABILITIES

Average female Guernsey cow.

### BAT-ZOO

While the pets in the Batcave are supposed to belong to Robin, Alfred Pennyworth seems to take on the lion's share of the work when it comes to feeding and caring for Bat-Cow, whether he's happy about it or not.

**Robin and Batman** were fighting villains in a slaughterhouse, when they realized it was an ambush. An assassin named Goatboy had tried and failed to destroy Robin. Taking pity on the last remaining cow, Robin declared himself a vegetarian and took the animal home with him. With mask-like coloring on his face and a star brand on his rump, Bat-Cow became Robin's newest pet.

*"Moo!"*

After Robin was killed by the villain Heretic, then brought back to life, he returned to the Batcave, happy that Alfred had taken care of his pets.

# THOMAS WAYNE

## VITAL STATS

**Full Name:** Thomas Wayne

**Occupation:** Surgeon, philanthropist

**Height:** 6ft 2in

**Weight:** 210 lbs

**Base:** Gotham City

**Allies:** Martha and Bruce Wayne, Alfred and Jarvis Pennyworth, Lucius Fox

**Foes:** Joe Chill, the Court of Owls

## POWERS AND ABILITIES

Highly skilled surgeon; powerful connections in the business world; amateur mechanic and inventor; extremely intelligent and loving father.

### THE LAST NIGHT

Thomas and Martha Wayne's fate was sealed the night they took their son to a screening of The Mark of Zorro in Gotham City. After the film, they were shot dead by Joe Chill during a botched robbery.

**Thomas Wayne was** a loving husband and father. Born into a wealthy family, Thomas created quite a career for himself as a surgeon. Though he was killed when his son Bruce was just a boy, he had nevertheless created many memories with his son, including showing Bruce a Witch's Eye, a hi-tech visual mapping device that later helped inspire the creation of the Batman.

*"What do you love about Gotham, Bruce?"*

Hat bears logo similar to Robin's

Wears casual attire in spare time when tinkering with mechanics

Doted on his son, often giving gifts

# MARTHA WAYNE

ALLY

## VITAL STATS

**Full Name:** Martha Wayne
**Occupation:** Mother, philanthropist
**Height:** 5ft 4in
**Weight:** 108 lbs
**Base:** Gotham City
**Allies:** Thomas and Bruce Wayne, Alfred and Jarvis Pennyworth
**Foes:** Joe Chill, the Court of Owls

## POWERS AND ABILITIES

Empathetic philanthropist; powerful contacts in Gotham City's most elite social circles, partially due to Kane family name (Martha's maiden name); intelligent and giving mother.

## MOTHER OF INNOVATION

Martha Wayne, a civic-minded woman, was upset at the state of Gotham City's education system. To fix the problem, she created a new school for Gotham City's underprivileged, despite receiving threats from the mayor's office.

**A loving mother** to Bruce Wayne, Martha Wayne was a philanthropist who stood up to Gotham City's corrupt mayor's office, not knowing it was backed by the violent, secret organization, the Court of Owls. The Court of Owls caused Martha to have a car "accident." and her loyal butler Jarvis Pennyworth was killed by a Talon assassin as well.

> **"You're the bravest boy in Gotham, Bruce."**

While her life was full of tragedy, and would soon end thanks to Joe Chill, Martha spent much of her short life doting on her son, Bruce.

# JAMES GORDON

## VITAL STATS

**Full Name:** James W. Gordon

**Occupation:** Deputized vigilante, former police commissioner

**Height:** 5ft 9in

**Weight:** 168 lbs

**Base:** Gotham City

**Allies:** Batman, the Batman Family, Batgirl, G.C.P.D.

**Foes:** The Joker, Mr. Bloom, James Gordon, Jr.

## POWERS AND ABILITIES

Extremely physically fit; natural leader; expertise in police procedure; former marine; robotic suit armed with crime-fighting equipment.

## BATMAN 2.0

After the real Batman seemingly died, James Gordon stepped up to fill the role as a fully deputized agent of the law.

Wearing a Batsuit inside a giant bat-themed robot suit, the 46-year-old does his best to fill Batman's shoes.

**James Gordon** worked his way up the chain of command at the Gotham City Police Department, fighting corruption at every turn. He eventually became commissioner, but was framed for murder and incarcerated. Gordon's job was not waiting for him when he was exonerated. However, he accepted an offer from Geri Powers to become the G.C.P.D.'s official Batman instead.

*"Sometimes, you just have to get out and walk the beat."*

Haircut harks back to his days as a Marine

Shaved mustache to resemble Batman

Highly trained fighter

Got back in shape to become Batman

# MAGGIE SAWYER

## VITAL STATS

**Full Name:** Margaret Sawyer

**Occupation:** Commissioner of the G.C.P.D.

**Height:** 5ft 10in

**Weight:** 130 lbs

**Base:** Gotham City

**Allies:** Batwoman, G.C.P.D., Superman

**Foes:** Nocturna, Ceto

### POWERS AND ABILITIES

Excellent detective and commanding officer; expert knowledge of police procedure and policy; natural leader with strong moral compass; trained in hand-to-hand combat as well as with a firearm.

**ONE GOOD COP**
Maggie Sawyer is a tough cop who has worked her way up the career ladder through honest police work. She promoted fellow honest cop, Harvey Bullock, to leader of the newly established Batman task force.

**Commissioner Maggie Sawyer** got her start in police work as an officer in the Metropolis Police Department. She got her first real taste of Gotham City when she was bused to the city with fellow officers to assist during a superstorm and citywide blackout. It was there she met her future fiancée Kate Kane for the first time—who would also go on to become Batwoman.

*"I'll do my best for your city."*

Wears bulletproof vest when needed

Dresses casually, but business appropriate

Excellent marksman, not afraid to shoot

# HARVEY BULLOCK

## VITAL STATS

**Full Name:** Harvey Bullock

**Occupation:** G.C.P.D. detective

**Height:** 5ft 10in

**Weight:** 248 lbs

**Base:** Gotham City

**Allies:** James Gordon, G.C.P.D., Renee Montoya, Batman

**Foes:** Anarky, the Joker's Daughter, Dr. Death

## POWERS AND ABILITIES

Excellent detective; good fighter with street smarts; loyal friend to James Gordon; one of the few honest cops in Gotham City.

## BULLOCK'S LAW

As a rookie police officer, Bullock worked with James Gordon on several cases, including the emergence of Dr. Death. As a detective, he's come into his own, and is respected throughout the G.C.P.D.

**Harvey Bullock**, who has been working for the G.C.P.D. since the infamous citywide blackout, is one of Gotham City's clean cops, even if his appearance doesn't quite match his resumé. While he and Batman don't always see eye to eye, Bullock often worked with the Dark Knight, and now teams with the Dark Knight's successor, James Gordon, as head of Batman's task force team.

*"I don't trust anyone... except you, Jimbo."*

Harvey trained G.C.P.D. officer Renee Montoya and they became friends—before she moved to Blüdhaven. She has since returned.

# RENEE MONTOYA

ALLY

## VITAL STATS

**Full Name:** Renee Montoya

**Occupation:** G.C.P.D. detective

**Height:** 5ft 8in

**Weight:** 144 lbs

**Base:** Gotham City

**Allies:** Harvey Bullock, Batman, James Gordon, Batwoman

**Foes:** Detective Nancy Yip, the Joker's Daughter

## POWERS AND ABILITIES

Highly trained police detective; trained by Harvey Bullock; experienced fighter with good hand-to-hand combat skills.

## A QUESTION OF ETHICS

While Renee Montoya has proven herself an honest police officer and fiercely loyal to other good cops, she's not above the occasional bar brawl. Especially when those she's trading punches with are known criminals.

**In the Gotham City** Police Department, it can often be hard to find cops on the right side of the law. While things have improved over the years thanks to James Gordon, that wasn't always the case. Corruption was rife in the department when Renee Montoya first started out, but she was determined to make a difference, aided and abetted by her instructor, Harvey Bullock.

*"...you know how sacred partnerships are."*

Back in Gotham City after years in Blüdhaven, Montoya wanted to root out corruption, and found an enemy in Detective Nancy Yip.

# G.C.P.D.

## VITAL STATS

**Official Name:** Gotham City Police Department

**Base:** Gotham City

**Allies:** Batman, the Batman Family, Batwoman

**Foes:** Criminals, Arkham Asylum inmates, Blackgate Penitentiary prisoners

**Notable Members:** James Gordon, Maggie Sawyer, Harvey Bullock, Renee Montoya, Carlos Alvarez, Travis Nie, Tammy Keyes, Jim Corrigan, Melody McKenna, Henry Wallace, Nancy Strode, Jack Forbes (former), Jason Bard (former), Nancy Yip (former), Gillian B. Loeb (former)

## POWER PLAY

Perhaps the best known commissioner in Gotham City's history, James Gordon was recently framed for a crime he didn't commit, and jailed until his eventual pardon. He now serves in the Batman task force under Commissioner Sawyer.

**The Gotham City Police** Department has a reputation for being corrupt. However, James Gordon has significantly curbed the institution's own criminal population. Now operating under the incorruptible commissioner, Maggie Sawyer, the G.C.P.D. employs dedicated men and women who are constantly at odds with the city's most notorious criminals, like Catwoman.

*"...Gotham isn't like any other city... We need Batman."*

Left to right: Detective Harvey Bullock, Commissioner Maggie Sawyer, and former commissioners Jack Forbes and Jason Bard.

# THE MIDNIGHT SHIFT

## VITAL STATS

**Real Name:** Precinct 13
**Base:** Gotham City
**Allies:** Batman, G.C.P.D.
**Foe:** Gentleman Ghost

**Members:** Lieutenant Sam Weaver, Detective Jim Corrigan, Detective Lisa Drake, Dr. Szandor Tarr, Sister Justine (deceased)

### THE 13TH PRECINCT

The G.C.P.D.'s most mysterious division, Precinct 13 is also referred to as the Midnight Shift. When its methods came into question, Sergeant Rook from internal affairs was assigned to assess the team.

**The Midnight Shift was** formed by Gotham City's former police commissioner, Jim Gordon. With its own discretionary budget, the task force was assembled to take care of "detailed cases." They deal with supernatural situations too bizarre for normal police officers, from battling mysterious entities, such as the Gentleman Ghost, to freeing possessed school children.

*"We're the guys who handle the strange stuff."*

Batman is aware of Jim Corrigan's dark secret: that he is host to Spectre, the angel of vengeance, and fights a daily battle to contain the spirit.

# LUCIUS FOX

## VITAL STATS

**Full Name:** Lucius Fox
**Occupation:** CEO of Wayne Enterprises
**Height:** 6ft
**Weight:** 199 lbs
**Base:** Gotham City
**Allies:** Batman and Bruce Wayne, Batwing, the Batman Family
**Foes:** Clayface, Ratcatcher, Menace

## POWERS AND ABILITIES

Savvy inventor and electronics expert; extremely intelligent and loyal to the Wayne family; near unlimited access to Wayne Enterprises' assets; financial genius.

### BATMAN BEYOND

When Fox was kidnapped by Clayface, Bruce Wayne saved his life with the help of an incredible prototype Batsuit. Unfortunately, Fox claimed that it wouldn't be cost effective for 20 years.

**While Lucius Fox spends** most of his time running the day to day operations of Bruce Wayne's huge company, he maintains a healthy interest in the Research & Development department, working with Batman to help the Dark Knight stay technologically innovative. Lucius is also the father of the hero Batwing, although he is unaware of his son Luke's crime-fighting career.

*"You came back to a city about five minutes before it collapsed."*

Inventor's mind has designed much of Batman's equipment

Unassuming appearance masks incredible intellect

Business attire for many important meetings

# GERI POWERS

## VITAL STATS

**Full Name:** Geri Powers

**Occupation:** CEO of Powers International

**Height:** 5ft 5in

**Weight:** 119 lbs

**Base:** Gotham City

**Allies:** .G.C.P.D, James Gordon

**Foe:** Mayor Sebastian Hady

### POWERS AND ABILITIES

CEO of one of the most powerful businesses in Gotham City and the world; oversees the technology for G.C.P.D.'s Batman project; powerful police and business connections; highly intelligent and motivated.

### THE POWER BEHIND THE BATMAN

Geri Powers oversaw the creation and implementation of the robotic armored Batsuit that James Gordon pilots in conjunction with the Gotham City Police Department. She helps Gordon get used to his new role and is his biggest supporter.

**Powers International has** been one of the most important corporations in Gotham City for centuries. After Wayne Enterprises was made defunct during a scheme launched by Lincoln March and the Cluemaster, Powers acquired the company and its assets. CEO Geri Powers gave the G.C.P.D. the technology to create a Batman of its own when the real Batman was presumed dead.

*"Are you ready to be Batman... Commissioner Gordon?"*

Gordon agreed to adopt the mantle of Batman after Powers pointed out that none of the G.C.P.D.'s recruits would be the "right" Batman.

# PHILIP KANE

## VITAL STATS

**Full Name:** Philip Kane
**Occupation:** Former Wayne Enterprises CEO
**Height:** 5ft 11in
**Weight:** 184 lbs
**Base:** Gotham City
**Allies:** The Riddler, Bruce Wayne, Martha Wayne
**Foes:** The Red Hood Gang

## POWERS AND ABILITIES

Access to Wayne Enterprises funds and technology; criminal ties to the Red Hood Gang; held powerful business connections; gifted eye for business; advised by Edward Nygma.

### KANE AND ABLE

The brother of Bruce Wayne's mother, Martha Wayne, Philip Kane had been trying to track Bruce down for years. Kane eventually located Bruce at his base, a townhouse near Crime Alley, the street where the Waynes were killed.

**When Thomas and Martha** Wayne were murdered and their son Bruce left to travel the world, Philip Kane was put in charge of the family business and merged Kane Chemical and Wayne Industries. On Bruce's return to Gotham City, he found out his uncle was working with the Red Hood Gang. After Kane's death at the hands of Red Hood One, Bruce reclaimed his company.

*"I never meant for things to turn out this way."*

On the night Batman foiled the Red Hood Gang's raid of A.C.E. Chemical, Philip Kane was killed by Red Hood One after trying to save Batman.

# HENRI DUCARD

## VITAL STATS

**Full Name:** Henri Ducard

**Occupation:** Mercenary

**Height:** 5ft 8in

**Weight:** 164 lbs

**Base:** Paris, France

**Allies:** NoBody

**Foe:** Batman

## POWERS AND ABILITIES

One of the world's best manhunters; expert in many lethal weapons as well as in hand-to-hand combat; numerous connections in the intelligence and criminal world.

## ETHICAL DISPUTES

Bruce Wayne discovered that he didn't always agree with his mentor's methods. During Bruce's training, they tracked down a terrorist named Hassan. Ducard assassinated Hassan instead of handing him over to the authorities, a decision Bruce did not approve of.

**Henri Ducard was** an accomplished manhunter, perhaps the best in the world. So unsurprisingly, when Bruce Wayne was training to become Batman, he sought out Ducard as one of his instructors. Henri agreed to train Wayne, seeing something he liked in the young man. He taught Bruce how to track and locate a man, a skill Batman has used throughout his career.

*"...it costs a lot to play in my game..."*

After the assassination of Hassan, Bruce ended his training with Ducard. Ducard was furious and sent his son, Morgan, to kill him.

# DUKE THOMAS

## VITAL STATS

**Full Name:** Duke Thomas

**Occupation:** Hero

**Height:** 5ft 6in

**Weight:** 129 lbs

**Base:** Gotham City

**Allies:** Batman, Alfred Pennyworth, fellow Robins, Julie Madison, Leslie Thompkins

**Foes:** The Joker, the Riddler

## POWERS AND ABILITIES

Incredibly intelligent and a good problem solver; natural leader; athletic and a good hand-to-hand combatant; access to Robin equipment and the Nest network.

## A DEBT OF GRATITUDE

After regaining consciousness after being cared for by Duke's family, Batman saved Duke Thomas from masked criminals. It was his way of paying the boy back for the kindness his family had shown him.

**Duke Thomas first met** Bruce Wayne during Gotham City's infamous blackout. With the Riddler taking control of the city, Duke's family nursed Wayne back to health and young Duke tried to devise a way to defeat the villain. Years later, Duke and Batman's met again when the Joker went after Duke's parents. Duke later went on to become Robin.

*"Don't you guys have professionals to do this kind of stuff?!"*

Still thinks about, and searches for, his missing parents

Each Robin wears colors in a unique way

Joined up with team of Robins led by Alfred

# VICKI VALE

## VITAL STATS

**Full Name:** Vicki Vale

**Occupation:** Journalist for the *Gotham Gazette*

**Height:** 5ft 8in

**Weight:** 115 lbs

**Base:** Gotham City

**Allies:** Bruce Wayne, Jason Bard, Warren Stacey

**Foes:** The Penguin, Carmine Falcone

## POWERS AND ABILITIES

Ace reporter with a knack for finding major news stories; extremely intelligent and a detective in her own right; athletic and capable of self-defense against attackers.

### HANDS ON

Unafraid to get her hands dirty while on the hunt for a scoop, Vicki once lashed out at a would-be mugger, holding a taser to his face in order to get information from the hardened criminal.

**Vicki Vale is one of** the *Gotham Gazette*'s most respected reporters. While she's usually particular about her sources and their credibility, she was once manipulated by former police lieutenant Jason Bard to cast him as a hero in the eyes of Gotham City's public. While her articles landed her a promotion, it took a lot of apologizing from Bard to win back her trust.

Vicki Vale has several ethical coworkers at the *Gotham Gazette*, including crime editor Warren Stacey.

*"It's insane...but not impossible."*

# MAYOR SEBASTIAN HADY

## VITAL STATS

**Full Name:** Sebastian Hady
**Occupation:** Mayor of Gotham City
**Height:** 5ft 6in
**Weight:** 202 lbs
**Base:** Gotham City
**Allies:** G.C.P.D., the Penguin, Carmine Falcone
**Foes:** James Gordon, Batman, Batman, Inc.

## POWERS AND ABILITIES

Wealthy connections; control over Gotham City's police department; persuasive and influential networker.

### MONEY ON HIS MIND

With a mind for money, Mayor Hady is quick to act in his own selfish interests. He once made a deal with Caldwell Technologies, not realizing their CEO was a super-villain known as Wrath.

**Gotham City is a corrupt** metropolis, so it only follows that its leader, Mayor Sebastian Hady, is an unethical and unapologetic individual. Hady originally ran for mayor in the year Batman first began to operate in Gotham City. These days, Hady doesn't shy away from working hand in hand with organized criminals, including the Penguin.

*"Batman is no longer welcome in Gotham City."*

Puts on a phony demeanor to appear likeable

Has gained weight since his campaign years

Well-dressed to look the part

# DR. LESLIE THOMPKINS

## VITAL STATS

**Full Name:** Dr. Leslie Thompkins
**Occupation:** Medical doctor
**Height:** 5ft 7in
**Weight:** 130 lbs
**Base:** Gotham City
**Allies:** Batman and Bruce Wayne, the Batman Family, Catwoman
**Foes:** The Fist of Cain cult

## POWERS AND ABILITIES

Skilled and knowledgeable doctor and surgeon; compassionate personality; opinionated with strong pacifist views; commands loyalty and respect; well-traveled and experienced.

### ADOPTING STRAYS

With a passion for helping wayward youth, Dr. Leslie Thompkins helped Catwoman years ago. She also helped a young Jason Todd, even after the young boy tried to steal from her clinic.

**Dr. Leslie Thompkins** was there for Bruce Wayne the night his parents were murdered. She comforted him, and built a trust that would last into his career as Batman. One night, when he was badly injured, Batman came to Dr. Thompkins at her clinic, and she discovered his alter ego. Since then, she has helped Batman, even if she sometimes disagrees with his methods.

> *"But you have to keep believing."*

Leslie took an interest in student Duke Thomas's life after his parents went missing, and helped place him in a few different foster homes.

# THE HUNTRESS

## VITAL STATS

**Real Name:** Helena Bertinelli

**Occupation:** Head of Spyral, Headmistress at finishing school

**Height:** 5ft 11in

**Weight:** 130 lbs

**Base:** Saint Hadrian's Finishing School for Girls, England

**Allies:** Dick Grayson, the Hood, Agent 1

**Foes:** Mr. Minos

## POWERS AND ABILITIES

Highly skilled martial artist and fighter; expert at espionage and natural leader.

### LOVE BIRDS?

Dick Grayson and Helena Bertinelli quickly became close allies in the field. They have learnt to trust each other in life-and-death situations, and it is becoming apparent that the two may want more than a professional partnership.

**Helena Bertinelli is the reason** Dick Grayson is working for the spy agency known as Spyral. Having vouched for the new recruit to the then head of the agency, Mr. Minos, Helena became partners with Grayson in his new role as Agent 37. However, when Helena discovered how corrupt Minos was, she put an arrow through him in order to protect her agency's secrets.

Equipped with mind-influencing "hypnos"

Has face-altering identity protection implants

Expert crossbow sharp shooter

*"From now on...I am Spyral."*

# SPYRAL

## VITAL STATS

**Team Name:** Spyral

**Base:** Saint Hadrian's Finishing School, England

**Allies:** Network of secret agents

**Foes:** Batman, Dick Grayson, Batman, Inc.

**Notable Members:** Dick Grayson, the Huntress, Dr. Dedalus, El Gaucho, The Hood, Mr. Minos, Frau Netz, Dr. Poppy Ashemore, Tiger

### WHO WATCHES THE WATCHMEN?
During his time as the head of Spyral, Mr. Minos kept tabs on all the world's superhumans, aided by one of his top scientists, and the daughter of Dr. Dedalus, Frau Netz.

**Originally founded by** Nazi scientist Otto Netz (Dr. Dedalus), Spyral is a clandestine agency that was led for many years by the enigmatic Mr. Minos, with the goal of gathering information on the superhuman community. When the corrupt nature of Minos's mission was revealed, he was dethroned by agent Helena Bertinelli who took over as head of the organization.

*"Power cannot be masked."*

Helena Bertinelli works with Dick Grayson as Agent 37, but doesn't realize that he has been secretly supplying Spyral information to Batman.

# AMADEUS ARKHAM

NEUTRAL

## VITAL STATS

**Full Name:** Amadeus Arkham

**Occupation:** Doctor of psychology

**Height:** 5ft 10in

**Weight:** 169 lbs

**Base:** Gotham City

**Allies:** Jonah Hex, Alan and Catherine Wayne

**Foes:** The Court of Owls, Religion of Crime

## POWERS AND ABILITIES

Highly trained psychologist; extremely intelligent; many connections in Gotham City's high society.

### A MAN OF LETTERS

Dr. Amadeus Arkham kept many journals that detailed his own history and, later, his descent into madness. While he was the founder of Arkham Asylum, he would also end up as one of its disturbed patients.

**A prominent doctor in** Gotham City in 1880, Amadeus Arkham worked directly with infamous bounty hunter, Jonah Hex, when a serial killer went on a terrifying spree through the city. Amadeus later transformed his large family estate into Arkham Asylum, the notorious home away from home of such modern day villains as the Joker, Two-Face, and Clayface.

*"...my interest lies in the inner workings of the mind."*

Amadeus Arkham and Jonah Hex went on many missions together. Jonah was annoyed by Amadeus at first, but he grew to respect him.

## VITAL STATS

**Full Name:** Jeremiah Arkham

**Occupation:** Director of Arkham Asylum

**Height:** 5ft 11in

**Weight:** 175 lbs

**Base:** Gotham City

**Allies:** Aaron Cash, G.C.P.D., Jonah Hex

**Foes:** The Court of Owls, Arkham Asylum inmates

### POWERS AND ABILITIES

Highly trained psychologist; extremely intelligent; many connections in Gotham City's political world.

### A PATH TO HEALING

Although stern, Dr. Jeremiah Arkham has not yet grown jaded from his position as the director of Arkham Asylum. He remains steadfast in the belief that he can cure the many unstable patients who reside there.

**Jeremiah Arkham's great-great** grandfather was Amadeus Arkham, Arkham Asylum's founder. Despite a family history of insanity, Jeremiah dedicated his life to rehabilitating the city's worst offenders. Normally preferring a position on the sidelines, Arkham was forced on an adventure when a time-traveling Jonah Hex escaped custody and kidnapped him.

Aaron Cash is another member of Arkham Asylum's staff. A hard-as-nails guard, he works tirelessly to keep the inmates in line.

*"...it sounds crazy, but...that's the Arkham family business."*

## VITAL STATS

**Full Name:** Alan Wayne

**Occupation:** Railroad tycoon, socialite and investor

**Height:** 5ft 11in

**Weight:** 171 lbs

**Base:** Gotham City

**Allies:** Catherine Wayne, Theodore Cobblepot, Edward Elliot, Cameron Kane, Amadeus Arkham

**Foes:** The Court of Owls, Nicholas and Bradley Gates

### POWERS AND ABILITIES

Influential Gotham City socialite with powerful connections; extremely wealthy and intelligent.

### DEATH OF THE FATHER

In 1922, Alan Wayne was held captive in the Court of Owls's underground labyrinth. When he emerged from the sewers, he ran straight into the arms of police officers before being killed by a Talon assassin.

**Alan Wayne was the** son of Judge Solomon Wayne, one of Gotham City's founders. Solomon had hired architect Cyrus Pinkney to build the city's first tall buildings and now Alan wanted to build even more. He hired architect brothers Nicholas and Bradley Gates to enhance the city's skyline, including building Wayne Tower. Alan was later killed by a Talon of the Court of Owls.

*"They're...coming for me!"*

Alan, Bruce Wayne's great, great grandfather, and his wife Catherine took an active role in Gotham City's social issues.

# JASON BARD

NEUTRAL

## VITAL STATS

**Full Name:** Jason Bard

**Occupation:** Former G.C.P.D. commissioner

**Height:** 6ft

**Weight:** 175 lbs

**Base:** Gotham City

**Allies:** Hush, Vicki Vale, James Gordon

**Foes:** Mayor Sebastian Hady, Carmine Falcone, Batman

## POWERS AND ABILITIES

Well-trained and highly intelligent police officer; finely-honed detective skills; connections to *Gotham Gazette* as well as to some of the worst criminals in Gotham City; keen strategist.

### SETTING HIS SIGHTS ON BATMAN

Jason Bard received inaccurate information from Hush, which pointed to huge cover-ups perpetrated by Wayne Enterprises and Batman. Bard set out on a mission to reveal the "truth" and expose Batman.

**Jason Bard was** a Detroit police officer until his partner was killed in a battle with a vigilante who was imitating Batman. That night, Bard—furious at the real Batman—was approached by Batman's long-time foe, Hush. Hush used his connections to place Bard in the G.C.P.D., where he rose through the ranks to the position of commissioner.

*"And that's how you take down a vigilante."*

Batman has always respected Bard as a top detective. After many confrontations with Batman, Bard discovered the error of his ways.

# GOTHAM ACADEMY STUDENTS

NEUTRAL

## VITAL STATS

**Student body includes:**

Olive Silverlock,

Mia "Maps" Mizoguchi,

Kyle Mizoguchi,

Pomeline Fritch,

Colton Rivera,

Eric Jorgensen,

Tristan Grey,

Damian Wayne (expelled)

## THE DETECTIVE CLUB

Olive Silverlock, her friend "Maps" Mizoguchi, and Maps's brother Kyle are three of Gotham Academy's shining stars. Together they formed a Detective Club that investigates some of the strange happenings around campus.

**One of Gotham City's** most influential private schools, Gotham Academy boasts some impressive alumni. Bruce Wayne himself spent some time there as a student. These days, the school has a varied student body, including a young man cursed with the Langstrom Man-Bat virus, Tristan Grey, and Olive Silverlock, a teen who has the ability to produce and control fire.

*"Every stone in these old walls has a story."*

Olive is haunted by the fact that her late mother spent time in Arkham Asylum. But regardless, she makes friends, including youthful Maps.

# GOTHAM ACADEMY FACULTY

## VITAL STATS

**Faculty includes:**

Headmaster
"Hammerhead" Hammer,
Professor Isla MacPherson,
Professor Hugo Strange,
Dr. Kirk Langstrom,
Coach Humphreys,
Mr. Scarlett,
"Aunt" Harriet,
Mr. Trent,
Professor Achilles Milo
(former teacher)

### THE CUSTODIAN

Gotham Academy is steeped in legends, one of which is the story of the Custodian, a mysterious hero who stalks the campus grounds, fighting off threats. In reality, the Custodian is really Headmaster Hammer protecting his students.

Professor Isla MacPherson

**Gotham Academy is** a prestigious boarding school that has attracted expert teachers from many different walks of life. There are science classes taught by the Man-Bat, Dr. Kirk Langstrom, and Professor Milo. Another Professor, Hugo Strange, serves as the school's counselor and there's "Bookworm" Mr. Scarlett, as well as kindly "Aunt" Harriet.

Mr. Scarlett, the school "Bookworm"

*"Welcome to Gotham Academy."*

Headmaster "Hammerhead" Hammer

# HALY'S CIRCUS

## VITAL STATS

**Group Name:**
Haly's Circus

**Base:** Mobile

**Allies:** Dick
Grayson, the
Court of Owls

**Foes:** Tony Zucco,
the Joker

**Notable Former
Members:**
C.C. Haly,
Dick Grayson,
John Grayson, Mary
Grayson, Bryan Haly,
Raya Vestri, Talon (Calvin
Rose), Talon (William
Cobb), Strix, Saiko

### GOTHAM CITY NO MORE
For years, Haly's Circus
made Gotham City a
staple on its tour route.
However, when two
members of its star
act, the Flying Graysons,
were killed by gangster
Tony Zucco, the circus
didn't return to the city
for almost five years.

**From all appearances**, Haly's Circus
seems like an innocent institution, a
touring group of performers with an
extensive history. But most customers
are unaware of the dark secret that
lurks beneath the surface. Decades
ago, the nefarious Court of Owls
made a deal with Haly's to recruit the
circus's best and brightest stars to
serve as the Court's Talon assassins.

*"Ladies and gentlemen...the star
of Haly's Circus...Dick Grayson!"*

A star member of the Flying Graysons trapeze
act, Dick was a prime target for the Court of
Owls, but he managed to escape life as a Talon.

# BARBARA KEAN GORDON

## VITAL STATS

**Full Name:** Barbara Kean Gordon

**Occupation:** Unknown

**Height:** 5ft 7in

**Weight:** 145 lbs

**Base:** Unknown coast, formerly Gotham City

**Allies:** Batgirl, James Gordon

**Foes:** James Gordon, Jr., the Joker

## POWERS AND ABILITIES

Intelligent but troubled; excellent baker.

## BUILDING BRIDGES

It took a while before Barbara Kean Gordon could earn the forgiveness of her daughter. But after Barbara Gordon discovered why her mother really left, she let her mom back into her life.

**Barbara Kean Gordon** left her husband, James Gordon, and their two children, Barbara Gordon and James Gordon, Jr., after James, Jr. killed the family cat, and threatened his sister, too. Although James, Jr. was just a child, his mother believed his threats. Years later she returned and attempted to rekindle a relationship with her daughter, who had become Batgirl.

*"Don't you recognize me, Barbara? I'm your mother."*

Barbara Kean Gordon confronted her son upon her return to Gotham City. She wounded him and watched her daughter, Batgirl, defeat him.

# JULIE MADISON

**ALLY**

## VITAL STATS

**Full Name:** Julie Madison

**Occupation:** Instructor at Lucius Fox Center for Gotham Youth

**Height:** 5ft 4in

**Weight:** 120 lbs

**Base:** Gotham City

**Allies:** Bruce Wayne, Lucius Fox

**Foe:** Mr. Bloom

### POWERS AND ABILITIES

Extremely intelligent, witty, and creative; powerful connections in Gotham City.

### A NEW START

With no memory of being Batman, Bruce Wayne is content in his life with Julie. Working together at the Lucius Fox Center for Gotham Youth, Wayne and Julie are visited by James Gordon, who has taken on the role of Batman.

**Julie Madison was** one of Bruce Wayne's first girlfriends. Dating back in their school years, they formed a strong bond that soon faded due to Bruce's focus on his mission and his obsession with his parents' death. When Batman was presumed dead and James Gordon took up his duties, Julie returned to Bruce's life, and they rekindled their old flame.

*"It's okay. Come on, let's go home."*

Bruce hated having to choose between Julie and his life as Batman. When he made his choice, Alfred had to tell Julie that Bruce was spoken for.

# HOLLY ROBINSON

NEUTRAL

## VITAL STATS

**Full Name:** Holly Robinson
**Occupation:** Former Hero
**Height:** 5ft 3½in
**Weight:** 115 lbs
**Base:** Mobile
**Allies:** Catwoman, Slam Bradley, Harley Quinn
**Foes:** Black Mask, Film Freak

## POWERS AND ABILITIES

Extremely fit and agile; adept hand-to-hand combatant with an emphasis on boxing techniques; proficient in the use of Catwoman's equipment.

### CATWOMAN IN TRAINING

Holly Robinson feels a true love for Gotham City's East End, and felt the need to protect it during Catwoman's brief retirement. Unfortunately, she never quite settled into the demanding role.

**Holly Robinson grew up** in a troubled home, and eventually ran away to try living on her own in Gotham City's East End. With a rough road ahead of her, Holly was fortunate enough to befriend Selina Kyle, and learned of Selina's fledgling career as the cat burglar Catwoman. Holly even briefly donned the Catwoman costume herself when Selina temporarily retired.

*"Gee, it truly is a glamorous profession!"*

Quick-witted and fast to react to danger

Slight build enables stealth

Thin frame from her life living on the streets

# THE JUSTICE LEAGUE

## VITAL STATS

**Team Name:** The Justice League

**Base:** Watchtower satellite in Earth's orbit

**Allies:** Black Lightning, the Teen Titans, Black Canary

**Foes:** Darkseid, Anti-Monitor, the Crime Syndicate

**Members:**
Batman, Superman, Wonder Woman, Aquaman, Green Lantern (Hal Jordan), the Flash, Cyborg, Shazam, Power Ring, Martian Manhunter (former), Firestorm (former), Element Woman (former), Atomica (traitor), Lex Luthor, Captain Cold

### NEW PARTNERSHIPS
It took some time for the founding Justice League members to trust one another. Some members, like Batman and Superman, began working together as partners outside of their Justice League missions.

**The Justice League** first formed when the other-dimensional tyrant Darkseid attempted to conquer Earth. Batman, Wonder Woman, Superman, Green Lantern, Cyborg, Aquaman, and the Flash successfully fought back, and decided to team up to battle other large-scale threats. Their roster has changed a few times, but they remain unwavering in their mission.

*"You can call us... the Super Seven!"*

The Justice League inducted "reformed" villains, Lex Luthor and Captain Cold, into their ranks after Luthor helped defeat the Crime Syndicate.

# SUPERMAN

## VITAL STATS

**Real Name:** Clark Kent, Kal-El

**Occupation:** Hero, reporter

**Height:** 6ft 3in

**Weight:** 235 lbs

**Base:** Metropolis

**Allies:** The Justice League, Steel, Supergirl, Superboy

**Foes:** Lex Luthor, Doomsday, Parasite, Darkseid

## POWERS AND ABILITIES

Super-strength; super-speed; superhuman reflexes, senses, durability, and endurance; flight; heat vision; X-ray vision; freeze breath; solar flare; extremely intelligent; access to advanced Kryptonian technology; powers derived from Earth's yellow sun.

**BREAK THE CHAINS**
Superman is a match for any hero or villain. Green Lantern quickly learned this fact during the formation of the Justice League, when he tried and failed to restrain the Man of Steel with green energy constructs.

Kryptonian costume was found on alien conqueror Brainiac's ship

S-Shield is the symbol of his Kryptonian family

Superman's cape is indestructible

**Baby Kal-El** was rocketed to Earth when his planet, Krypton, exploded. Discovered by the Kent family, the infant was renamed Clark. As he matured, Clark discovered that Earth's yellow sun gave him awesome abilities. He soon put these powers to use in order to protect his adopted city of Metropolis as the ultimate Super Hero, Superman.

*"Treat people right or expect a visit from me."*

# CLARK KENT

## VITAL STATS

**Full Name:** Clark Kent, Kal-El

**Occupation:** Hero, reporter

**Height:** 6ft 3in

**Weight:** 235 lbs

**Base:** Metropolis

**Allies:** Lois Lane, Jimmy Olsen, Perry White, Bruce Wayne

**Foes:** Lex Luthor, Doomsday, Parasite, Darkseid

### POWERS AND ABILITIES

Extremely intelligent; access to contacts from the world of journalism; mild-mannered persona created to deflect attention; excellent investigative skills.

## SEEKER OF TRUTH

Beginning his career at the *Daily Star*, Clark Kent wrote intriguing and fearless exposés. He befriended the wealthy Jimmy Olsen in the process, as well as his longtime crush, another ace reporter, Lois Lane.

**Everybody knows that** Clark Kent grew up in Smallville, Kansas, and was raised by Jonathan and Martha Kent. But for years, Clark hid the fact that he is an alien from the distant planet Krypton. Clark was sent to Earth by his birth parents, Jor-El and Lara, when his planet was destroyed. Clark dedicates his career to truth as a reporter for the *Daily Planet*.

*"I've waited my whole life for this."*

Since most people don't think Superman has time for a secret life, his idea of hiding in plain sight, behind a pair of glasses, works perfectly.

# SUPERGIRL

## VITAL STATS

**Real Name:** Kara Zor-El
**Occupation:** Hero
**Height:** 5ft 5in
**Weight:** 120 lbs
**Base:** Mobile
**Allies:** Superman, Superboy, the Justice League United, Steel
**Foes:** Jochi, Silver Banshee, H'el

## POWERS AND ABILITIES

Super-strength; super-speed; superhuman reflexes, durability, senses, and endurance; flight; heat vision; freeze breath; X-ray vision; access to advanced Kryptonian technology; powers derived from Earth's yellow sun.

### WORLD'S FINEST

In order to defeat the threat of the alien Jochi, Superman and Batman had to pick two champion allies to compete in Warworld's deadly gladiatorial arena. Superman chose Steel and Supergirl and Batman chose Red Hood and Batgirl.

**Kara Zor-El came from** a prestigious family who lived in Argo City, one of the biggest metropolises on planet Krypton. Her scientist father, Zor-El, was Jor-El's brother. As Jor-El built a rocket ship to allow his baby Kal-El to escape Krypton's destruction, Zor-El created an escape pod for his daughter. Kara found her way to Earth and adopted the guise of Supergirl.

*"You have to trust me to find my own way."*

Like Clark Kent, she has freeze breath

Wears the El family S-Shield

Can fly at high speeds

# WONDER WOMAN

## VITAL STATS

**Real Name:** Diana
**Occupation:** Hero, queen, God of War
**Height:** 6ft
**Weight:** 165 lbs
**Base:** Themyscira
**Allies:** Superman, Orion, the Justice League
**Foes:** Cheetah, Circe, the First Born

## POWERS AND ABILITIES

Godly blood grants her super-strength, endurance, and agility; power of flight; Bracelets of Victory can deflect bullets; expert fighter and strategist; Lasso of Truth forces others to tell the truth; extremely wise and empathetic.

## HEAR HER ROAR

Wonder Woman has occasionally changed her armor, but always retains the "star" iconography that represents her family lineage. An emissary of peace, she is also a true warrior at heart.

**Diana is the daughter** of the god Zeus and Hippolyta, the ruler of Themyscira, an island of female warriors called the Amazons. Diana grew up a princess completely isolated from the rest of the world. When a pilot named Steve Trevor crashed on Themyscira, Diana learned of the outside world and soon traveled there as her people's representative and a true Super Hero—Wonder Woman.

*"It's a big, strange, and wondrous universe."*

Armor forged by god Hephaestus

Tiara a sign of regal lineage

Bracelets of Victory can produce blades

Flexible armor for ease of movement

Lasso can be used to attack or defend

# AQUAMAN

## VITAL STATS

**Real Name:**
Arthur Curry

**Occupation:** Hero, king of Atlantis

**Height:** 6ft 1in

**Weight:** 325 lbs

**Base:** Atlantis

**Allies:** Mera, the Justice League, the Others

**Foes:** Black Manta, Ocean Master, the Trench

## POWERS AND ABILITIES

Can breathe underwater; can communicate with and control sea life; ruler of underwater kingdom of Atlantis; super-strength; trained fighter and natural leader; swims incredibly fast.

### FISH OUT OF WATER

Batman and Aquaman have fought side-by-side on many missions as part of the Justice League. The two have also teamed up as partners on occasion, including the time they battled Rās al Ghūl on a remote island in the Pacific.

**Arthur Curry was** born to a lighthouse keeper and an Atlantean queen, and raised on land when his mother returned to the sea. Thanks to his ability to breathe underwater and communicate with sea life, Arthur became known as Aquaman when he was a young man. The rightful king of Atlantis, he uses his abilities to fight for creatures on land and in the ocean.

> *"So who's in charge here? I vote me."*

Body can bear pressures of the deep

Blond hair rare in Atlantis

Wears scale-like uniform

Carries trident to use as weapon

# GREEN LANTERN

## VITAL STATS

**Real Name:** Harold (Hal) Jordan

**Occupation:** Hero

**Height:** 6ft 2in

**Weight:** 186 lbs

**Base:** Mobile, Coast City

**Allies:** The Justice League, Green Lantern Corps

**Foes:** Sinestro, Red Lanterns, Black Hand

## POWERS AND ABILITIES

Expert pilot; natural leader; Green Lantern ring can create physical manifestations of anything its user imagines; it also allows for flight, force fields, and space travel, and can impart encyclopedic knowledge to its wearer.

### EMERALD KNIGHT

Green Lantern and Batman first met during Darkseid's invasion of the Earth. Hal Jordan was surprised to learn that the Dark Knight possessed no special powers, and was simply Bruce Wayne in an armored uniform.

Ring creates Hal's mask and uniform

Responsible for protecting space sector 2814

Green power ring creates anything Hal can imagine

**As a child, Hal Jordan** idolized his pilot father, who died in a plane crash. Hal grew up to be just like his dad, overcoming his fear of flying and finding work at Ferris Airlines. When Abin Sur, a member of the galactic peacekeepers known as the Green Lanterns, crashed his spaceship on Earth, his magical ring chose Hal to replace Abin Sur as the newest member of the Green Lanterns.

*"You're not just some guy in a bat costume, are you?"*

# GREEN LANTERN

## VITAL STATS

**Real Name:** John Stewart

**Occupation:** Hero

**Height:** 6ft 1in

**Weight:** 210 lbs

**Base:** Mobile

**Allies:** Green Lantern Corps, Hal Jordan, Kilowog

**Foes:** Red Lantern Corps, Larfleeze, Sinestro Corps

## POWERS AND ABILITIES

Expert architect; military training; natural leader; Green Lantern ring can create physical manifestations of anything its user imagines; it also allows for flight, force fields, and space travel, and can impart encyclopedic knowledge to its wearer.

## THE LOGICAL LANTERN

John Stewart is a military man and a former architect. As such, he thinks logically and precisely. While some of his fellow Green Lanterns may conjure fanciful objects with their rings, John keeps his constructs efficient.

**The son of a political activist**, John Stewart grew up learning to fight for what's right—peacefully. He left home in Detroit, Michigan, to join the Marines, and helped with the relief effort during the superstorm that caused Gotham City's blackout. But after falling out with his superiors, John was honorably discharged, only to be enlisted in a greater army, the Green Lantern Corps.

*"This is the end of the road...just not for me."*

As a member of the intergalactic peacekeeping force, the Green Lantern Corps, John Stewart has finally found his purpose in life.

# CYBORG

## VITAL STATS

**Real Name:** Victor Stone

**Occupation:** Hero, scientist

**Height:** 6ft 5in

**Weight:** 385 lbs

**Base:** Detroit, Michigan

**Allies:** The Justice League, the Metal Men, S.T.A.R. Labs

**Foes:** Grid, the Crime Syndicate, Darkseid

## POWERS AND ABILITIES

Cybernetic body allows for enhanced endurance, durability, agility, speed, and strength; can tap into world grid allowing internet access; computer and robotics expert; adept hacker; naturally athletic and intelligent; hi-tech weapons include white-noise blaster.

## WORK IN PROGRESS

Cyborg is a founder of the Justice League, and was its youngest member until Shazam joined. After being attacked by the artificial life form known as Grid, Victor completely upgraded his cybernetic body.

**A star football player** in high school, Victor Stone was at odds with his father, who wanted Vic to pursue education over athletics. When Darkseid invaded Earth, Vic was mortally wounded, saved only when his father subjected him to an experimental cybernetic bonding process, turning him into a cyborg. Vic put his advanced artificial body to use, becoming a hero.

Can access internet with a mere thought

Robotic body is incredibly durable

Favors white noise blasts of energy

*"What am I?"*

# THE FLASH

## VITAL STATS

**Real Name:** Barry Allen

**Occupation:** Hero, forensic scientist

**Height:** 5ft 11in

**Weight:** 179 lbs

**Base:** Central City

**Allies:** The Justice League, Green Lantern, Iris West

**Foes:** Captain Cold, Mirror Master, Heatwave, Captain Boomerang

## POWERS AND ABILITIES

Draws super-speed powers from an extradimensional Speed Force energy; extremely intelligent; well-versed in police procedure and detection; skilled crime scene investigator.

## SPEED BUMPS

The Flash has gathered his own Rogues Gallery over the years, from villains like Heatwave, to murderers like the Keystone Killer. As the Flash, and as a crime scene investigator, he does his best to protect his city.

**When Barry Allen was** a boy, his mother died, and his father was arrested as the culprit. Desperate to get to the truth, Barry studied forensics, and later became a criminologist for the police. One night, a bolt of lightning struck a shelf of chemicals, splashing them onto Allen, giving him the power to move at fantastic speeds as the Flash.

*"No matter what—I'll never stop chasing the truth."*

Designed his own flame-colored costume

Costume can shrink small enough to fit inside a ring

Speed causes lightning to trail off behind him

# GREEN ARROW

HERO

## VITAL STATS

**Real Name:** Oliver Queen
**Occupation:** Hero, head of the Queen Foundation
**Height:** 5ft 11in
**Weight:** 185 lbs
**Base:** Seattle, Washington
**Allies:** The Justice League of America, Katana, Arsenal, Batman
**Foes:** Count Vertigo, Richard Dragon II, the Clock King

## POWERS AND ABILITIES

Expert archer with variety of arrows; skilled hand-to-hand combatant and martial artist.

### TAKING AIM

During his crime-fighting career, Green Arrow has amassed his own Rogues Gallery, from the team of Midas and Blood Rose, to the master martial artist Richard Dragon and the gang leader, the Clock King.

**Heir to the Queen fortune**, Oliver Queen lived a life of excess. Despite being trained from an early age in the art of the bow and arrow by his father, Robert, Oliver didn't embrace the skill until he was stranded on a deserted island for three years. Oliver eventually escaped from the island, and reemerged in Seattle a changed man, fighting criminals as the hero Green Arrow.

*"I won't let anyone else get hurt in this city because of me."*

Quiver filled with array of trick arrows

Armored suit helps protect from damage

Belt contains small crime-fighting tools

Bow also used as handle for zip lines

Shins and forearms have added armor

# MARTIAN MANHUNTER

## VITAL STATS

**Real Name:** J'onn J'onzz
**Occupation:** Hero
**Height:** 6ft 7in
**Weight:** 250 lbs
**Base:** Mobile
**Allies:** The Justice League of America, the Justice League, Stormwatch, the Justice League United
**Foes:** The Crime Syndicate, the Secret Society

## POWERS AND ABILITIES

Super-strength; super-speed; superhuman agility and endurance; invisibility; shape-shifting powers; flight; telepathy; Martian vision; able to pass through solid objects; highly intelligent and determined; natural leader.

### SUPER-MANHUNTER

The Martian Manhunter is one of the most powerful Super Heroes. Possessing most of the abilities of Superman, J'onn's shape-shifting, telepathy, and invisibility powers give him a huge advantage in any fight.

Can communicate with others by thought

Green skin a sign of Martian heritage

Costume can shape-shift with his flesh

Body can pass through solid objects

**The people of Mars** lived a connected life, communicating with each other through their thoughts. When J'onn J'onzz became their leader, he journeyed to another world to experience the feeling of being alone. When he returned he found Mars aflame. Believing he was the planet's sole survivor, he traveled to Earth to use his powers for good as the Martian Manhunter.

*"My friends call me J'onn..."*

# LEX LUTHOR

## VITAL STATS

**Full Name:** Lex Luthor

**Occupation:** CEO of LexCorp, criminal

**Height:** 6ft 2in

**Weight:** 210 lbs

**Base:** Metropolis

**Allies:** Captain Cold, the Justice League, Mercy Graves, Brainiac

**Foes:** Superman, the Crime Syndicate, Batman

## POWERS AND ABILITIES

Near unparalleled intellect; armored flight suit equipped with hi-tech weaponry and defenses; suit grants him superhuman strength and speed.

## INJUSTICE FOR ALL

After convincing the world he was a true hero by playing a major part in the defeat of the Crime Syndicate, Lex Luthor rallied public support to become a member of the Justice League.

**Lex Luthor first met** Superman whilst working with the United States government and the alien entity known as Brainiac. Wishing to be mankind's savior against the alien threat Superman presented, he helped capture and experiment on the Kryptonian hero but Superman escaped. Luthor has maintained a vendetta against Superman ever since.

Genius-level intellect and business savvy

Clothes suit his luxurious lifestyle

Dresses in business attire, when not in hero costume

*"I'm a changed man, Superman."*

# BLACK LIGHTNING

## VITAL STATS

**Real Name:** Jefferson Pierce
**Occupation:** Hero,
high school teacher
**Height:** 6ft 1in
**Weight:** 200 lbs
**Base:** Los Angeles,
California
**Allies:** Batman, Blue Devil,
the Justice League,
**Foe:** Tobias Whale

## POWERS AND ABILITIES

Can generate black
electricity from his own
body; Olympic-level athlete;
natural leader; excellent
teacher with a very
intelligent mind.

### BLACK AND BLUE
Black Lightning has been
known to team with the
magical hero Blue Devil.
Before the two were
Super Hero partners,
they were old high school
friends who played on
the same football team.

**Jefferson Pierce's father** is a reporter
who instilled a strong sense of right
and wrong in his son. Jefferson grew
up to become an Olympic gold medalist
in track and field, and later evolved
into the electricity-powered hero Black
Lightning. He formed a partnership
with Blue Devil and was even recruited
by Batman and the Justice League,
but chose not to become a member.

*"Never lose your focus
in a fight!"*

Visor hides
identity and
protects eyes

Costume
can generate
electricity too

Altered costume
to include gold
design

# THE OUTSIDERS

## VITAL STATS

**Team Name:** The Outsiders
**Base:** Gotham City
**Allies:** Batman, Batman, Inc., Alfred Pennyworth
**Foes:** Mr. Freeze, Clayface, Leviathan, Masters of Disaster

**Notable Members:**
Geo-Force, Halo, Katana, Metamorpho, Black Lightning, Looker, Red Robin, Freight Train, Owlman (Roy Raymond, Jr.)

### OUTSIDE HELP
When Batman was sent time traveling by the villain Darkseid, Alfred Pennyworth decided to unite his allies, the Outsiders, into a new team to pick up where the Dark Knight left off.

**The team of Super Heroes** called the Outsiders has shared a long history with Batman and his allies. United some time ago as Batman's personal strike force to go on missions the Justice League wouldn't touch, the Outsiders have proved themselves devoutly loyal to the Caped Crusader, repeatedly putting their lives on the line, even against the evil forces of Leviathan.

*"We're a low maintenance crowd."*

When uniting against the forces of Leviathan, Batman teamed the Outsiders with their new leader and his former partner, Red Robin.

# KATANA

## VITAL STATS

**Real Name:** Tatsu Toro

**Occupation:** Hero, assassin

**Height:** 5ft 2in

**Weight:** 96 lbs

**Base:** Japantown, San Francisco, California

**Allies:** The Birds of Prey, the Justice League of America, Batman

**Foes:** The Creeper, Coil, Killer Croc

## POWERS AND ABILITIES

Skilled martial artist with expertise in swordsmanship; communicates with deceased inhabitants of her sword.

## OUTSIDER ON THE INSIDE

Katana is often at odds with the Sword Clan crime family, including its deadly member Coil. She allied herself briefly with the Swords, but was never an official member as she was with the Justice League of America and the Birds of Prey.

**Tatsu Toro was torn** between her husband, Maseo Yamashiro, and his brother, Takeo, a martial artist. During a fight between them, Tatsu stepped in, accidentally killing Maseo and trapping his soul in the Soultaker sword. Tatsu dedicated her life to fighting and swordsmanship as Katana, maintaining a relationship with Maseo's trapped soul.

> **"...I am not here to make friends."**

Soultaker sword traps the souls of its victims

Wears colors of Japan's flag on her mask

Armored suit provides full-body protection

Armored patch protects against swords

Lightweight suit worn under casual clothing

# METAMORPHO

## VITAL STATS

**Real Name:** Rex Mason

**Occupation:** Hero, adventurer

**Height:** 6ft 1in

**Weight:** 200 lbs

**Base:** Haneyville

**Allies:** Batman, Inc., the Outsiders, Batman, Sapphire Stagg

**Foes:** Simon Stagg, Leviathan, Java

## POWERS AND ABILITIES

Can transform his body into any element or mix of elements found in the human body; brave explorer with loyal heart; superhuman recovery and endurance; knowledge of ancient artifacts.

## CURSE THE ELEMENTS

Despite possessing amazing powers that enable him to turn himself as hard as steel or as untouchable as a gas, Metamorpho simply wants to return to human form and continue his life with Sapphire Stagg.

**An adventurer who loved** a challenge, Rex Mason was in love with Sapphire Stagg, daughter of the wealthy and corrupt Simon Stagg. While exploring an ancient pyramid, Rex was betrayed by Stagg's henchman and exposed to a meteor that changed him into Metamorpho, the Element Man. He put his powers to good use as a member of Batman's Outsiders team.

Master of simultaneous transformations

Face and body stuck in bizarre colors

Can transform entire body or small sections

*"Always one step a—head."*

# GEO-FORCE

## VITAL STATS

**Real Name:** Brion Markov
**Occupation:** Ruler of Markovia
**Height:** 6ft 4in
**Weight:** 210 lbs
**Base:** Markovia
**Allies:** The Outsiders, Batman, Terra
**Foes:** Masters of Disaster, Clayface, Baron Bedlam

## POWERS AND ABILITIES

Projects lava blasts from hands; can increase or decrease gravity on himself or others; combines lava blast and gravity powers to propel himself via flight; superhuman strength, endurance, and durability; able to manipulate earth and rock.

### MOVER AND SHAKER

Due to the evil schemes of the villain Deathstroke, Geo-Force gained the ability of a so-called "earth-mover." This means he is able to control and manipulate rocks and dirt, abilities that complement his gravity powers.

**The Prince of the** Eastern European nation of Markovia, Brion Markov had a bright future ahead of him. A keen patriot, he volunteered himself for an experiment that gave him earth-themed powers. He adopted the identity of Geo-Force and became a founding member of the Outsiders. He is a loyal ally of the Dark Knight when not serving his country as its ruler.

*"...isn't it time for evil to be punished?"*

Brion became ruler of Markovia after the death of his brother. He now has the ability to protect his people from the throne and on the battlefield.

# HALO

## VITAL STATS

**Real Name:** Gabrielle Doe
**Occupation:** Hero
**Height:** 5ft 7in
**Weight:** 120 lbs
**Base:** Mobile
**Allies:** The Outsiders, Batman, Inc., Batman
**Foes:** Leviathan, Talia al Ghūl, Syonide II

## POWERS AND ABILITIES

Controls and manipulates visible energy, called an aura: red aura generates heat; orange aura projects force blasts; yellow aura generates light; green aura keeps things still; blue distortion aura causes illusions; indigo aura is a tractor beam; all auras enable flight and space travel.

### GROWING PAINS

As a member of the Outsiders, Halo matured from a naïve girl to a strong and independent young woman, often guided by the woman she saw as a mother figure, Katana.

**Before Batman gave her** the name Halo, the woman who would adopt the name of Gabrielle Doe wasn't a woman at all, but an Aurakle, a cosmic being from a race older than time itself. Curious about human life, this Aurakle reached out to a dying girl, Violet Harper, and found herself trapped in the girl's human form. She forgot her own past for a time and became Halo.

*"Halo here. Everything's okay."*

Halo's green aura is her stasis aura. It can freeze any living thing or chemical reaction in place, but it doesn't work on machines or affect gravity.

# SHAZAM!

## VITAL STATS

**Real Name:** Billy Batson

**Occupation:** Hero, student

**Height:** 6ft 1in

**Weight:** 195 lbs

**Base:** Philadelphia

**Allies:** The Justice League, Freddy Freeman

**Foes:** Black Adam, Mazahs, Dr. Sivana, Mr. Mind

## POWERS AND ABILITIES

Superhuman wisdom, courage, strength, endurance, agility, speed, senses, and durability; flight; ability to call down magic lightning; can transform from teen to adult by saying the magic word, "Shazam!"

## BLACK MAGIC

With one word, "Shazam!", teenager Billy Batson is transformed into a mystically-powered adult, controlling the power of living lightning. His abilities came in handy when forced to combat his would-be usurper, Black Adam.

Can share magic with others if he so chooses

Magic lightning bolt symbol constantly glows

Costume appears when he transforms

**An orphan, 15-year-old** Billy Batson was taken in by the kindly Vasquez family. One night, the subway car Billy was riding in magically took him to the Rock of Eternity where he met an old wizard. The wizard turned him into the Super Hero Shazam! After facing down the threat of villain Black Adam, Shazam put his powers to good use by joining the Justice League.

*"You picked the wrong person to push around."*

# THE JUSTICE LEAGUE OF AMERICA

## VITAL STATS

**Team Name:** The Justice League of America

**Base:** A.R.G.U.S. headquarters, Washington, D.C.

**Allies:** The Justice League, Amanda Waller

**Foes:** The Secret Society, the Crime Syndicate

**Members:** Colonel Steve Trevor, Catwoman, Katana, Green Arrow, Hawkman, Stargirl, Martian Manhunter, Green Lantern Simon Baz, Vibe, Dr. Light

## BOXING MATCH

Shortly after the Justice League of America formed, they fought the original Justice League over a relic called Pandora's Box. What they didn't realize was that the box opened a portal to the nefarious dimension Earth-Three.

With the teen icon Stargirl a member, the team was welcomed onto the Super Hero scene by the masses.

**Worried that the** Justice League did not operate under government control, the US government directed Amanda Waller to create an official US Super Hero team. Waller recruited Steve Trevor to lead the all-new Justice League of America. Ready to take down the original Justice League if required, the JLA was the country's first line of defense against superhuman threats.

*"We introduce the JLA to the world tomorrow."*

# THE TEEN TITANS

## VITAL STATS

**Team Name:** The Teen Titans

**Base:** New York City

**Allies:** The Batman Family, the Outlaws, S.T.A.R. Labs

**Foes:** Harvest, Trigon, Deathstroke

**Members:** Red Robin, Bunker, Beast Boy, Raven, Superboy, Wonder Girl (former), Power Girl (former), Kid Flash (former), Solstice (former), Skitter (former), Danny the Alley (former)

### S.T.A.R.S OF THE SHOW
When there's trouble, call the Teen Titans. The latest incarnation of the team began working hand in hand with the scientifically advanced S.T.A.R. Labs and includes Beast Boy, Red Robin, Bunker, and Raven.

**When teen heroes** were being captured by a villain called Harvest, Red Robin decided to recruit young metahumans and form a team of Super Heroes to combat the threat. He enlisted the help of Wonder Girl and other young heroes, including Kid Flash and Bunker. Together, they ended Harvest's reign of terror, and the team continues to fight injustice as the Teen Titans.

*"Maybe we can do great things together."*

Once an important member of the Teen Titans, Wonder Girl quit its ranks to lead a morally questionable team called the Elite.

**HEROES**

## VITAL STATS

**Team Name:** The Outlaws
**Base:** Unnamed, uncharted island
**Allies:** Batman, the Batman Family, Crux
**Foes:** Rā's al Ghūl, the Untitled, Suzie Su

**Members:**
Red Hood
Arsenal
Starfire

### AN ATTACK ON CRIME
The Outlaws often chose to pursue figures from the world of organized crime. One such unlucky individual was the Hong Kong crime lord known as Suzie Su, who didn't survive their last encounter.

**Green Arrow's former** partner Arsenal was imprisoned in in the eastern nation of Qura. He was rescued by the Super Hero Red Hood and Starfire, an alien princess from the planet Tamaran. The three set up a base in Starfire's marooned starship, forming a team called the Outlaws. Starfire later quit, leaving Red Hood and Arsenal to form a partnership.

*"We were friends, helping each other...we were outlaws!"*

Starfire, aka Princess Koriand'r

Arsenal, aka Roy Harper

Red Hood, aka Jason Todd

# RAGMAN

## VITAL STATS

**Real Name:** Rory Regan

**Occupation:** Hero, pawnshop owner

**Height:** 5ft 11in

**Weight:** 165 lbs

**Base:** Gotham City

**Allies:** Batwoman, the Unknowns, Batman

**Foe:** Morgaine le Fey

## POWERS AND ABILITIES

Wears suit of rags composed of evil souls; can absorb souls into his suit in order to stop corrupt individuals; granted strengths and knowledge of those imprisoned in his rags; superhuman agility, speed, and strength; can float on air currents.

### RAGTIME

The mysterious Ragman has teamed up with Batman in the past, and became a staunch ally of Batwoman as a fellow member of the Unknowns. He was integral in the defeat of evil sorceress Morgaine le Fey.

**By day, the owner** of the Rags 'n' Tatters pawnshop in Gotham City, Rory Regan does his best to help his neighbors in tough times. By night, he patrols the city in a mystical living suit of rags that summons him when he is needed. Rory's suit is actually a cloth "golem" of sorts, created by an ancient Council of Rabbis to protect the Jewish people.

*"I specialize in finding truths."*

Constantly struggling with the evil souls within his rags

Suit clothes him when he is needed

Rags surround and speak to him

Can be as light as rags, to float on wind

# THE JOKER

**ROGUE**

## VITAL STATS

**Real Name:** Unknown
**Occupation:** Criminal
**Height:** 6ft 5in
**Weight:** 192 lbs
**Base:** Gotham City
**Allies:** Harley Quinn, the Joker's Daughter, the Red Hood Gang
**Foes:** Batman, the Batman Family, James Gordon

### POWERS AND ABILITIES

Insanity causes unpredictable behavior; agile and a relentless fighter; twisted genius mind with expertise in chemistry; brilliant strategist; lacks moral code; employs clown-themed weapons; Venom gives his victims permanent grins.

### KILLER CLOWN FROM GOTHAM CITY

The Joker considers himself Batman's arch-enemy, and is virtually obsessed with the hero and his team. During his career, he has temporarily paralyzed Batgirl and killed Jason Todd, and even severed Alfred's hand.

**While his true identity** remains a mystery, the Joker is believed to have been the criminal known as Red Hood One, the man in charge of the Red Hood Gang. That chapter of his life ended when Batman took down his organization and knocked the criminal into a vat of chemicals. The Joker survived, albeit with severely altered features, including a damaged mind.

*"Just think of the great times we've had...and smile!"*

Uses razor-sharp playing cards as weapons

Hair dyed green from chemical exposure

Trademark purple suit with clashing shirt and tie

Employs deadly "jokes" like acid-squirting flowers

# HARLEY QUINN

**ROGUE**

## VITAL STATS

**Real Name:** Dr. Harleen Quinzel

**Occupation:** Criminal, landlord, roller derby participant

**Height:** 5ft 7in

**Weight:** 115 lbs

**Base:** Coney Island, Brooklyn, New York

**Allies:** The Joker, Suicide Squad, Poison Ivy, Scarecrow

**Foes:** Batman, the Batman Family

## POWERS AND ABILITIES

Insanity causes unpredictability; agile and capable fighter; employs dozens of clown-themed weapons and lackeys; often uses giant hammer as a weapon.

### LEFT HER HEART IN GOTHAM CITY

Putting Gotham City and her love affair with the Joker behind her, Harley Quinn moved to Coney Island and set up shop as a landlord, taking part in roller derbies.

**Harley Quinn was a** Gotham University graduate who began working at Arkham Asylum. To gain the inmates' trust, she dyed her hair two-toned and posed as a patient. The Joker saw through her ruse, and Harley found herself falling in love with him. They escaped Arkham, and the Joker threw her into a vat of chemicals to bleach her skin and cement their relationship.

*"Oh, Mistah J..."*

Enjoys the violence of roller derby

Adept at using trademark giant hammer

Skin bleached white thanks to the Joker

Not averse to using traditional guns

# THE PENGUIN

## VITAL STATS

**Real Name:** Oswald Chesterfield Cobblepot

**Occupation:** Crime boss, owner of the Iceberg Casino

**Height:** 5ft 2in

**Weight:** 175 lbs

**Base:** Gotham City

**Allies:** Lark, Catwoman, Mr. Toxic, Hypnotic, Mr. Combustible

**Foes:** Batman, the Batman Family, Black Canary

## POWERS AND ABILITIES

Master strategist; brilliant criminal mind; employs a variety of trick umbrellas; major underworld connections.

## OLD ENEMIES

Batman and the Penguin have a long history, going back to a time before either of them had adopted their animal-themed names. Batman often takes advantage of the Penguin's extensive criminal ties, scaring information out of the villain.

**Oswald Chesterfield Cobblepot** hails from one of Gotham City's oldest and most influential families, albeit a corrupt one. Determined to climb to the top of the heap, Oswald continued his family's legacy, dealing in illegal weapons. Now known as the Penguin, he rose to power in Gotham City's underworld, becoming a feared crime boss and owner of the Iceberg Casino.

*"Almost everything went according to plan, little birdie."*

Physical features resemble a penguin

White gloves coordinate with the spats on his shoes

Weapons are concealed in his umbrellas

Agile and violent despite his size

# SCARECROW

ROGUE

## VITAL STATS

**Real Name:** Dr. Jonathan Crane

**Occupation:** Criminal, former psychiatrist and college professor

**Height:** 6ft

**Weight:** 140 lbs

**Base:** Gotham City

**Allies:** The Secret Society, Professor Pyg, Merrymaker, Harley Quinn, Mr. Freeze

**Foes:** Batman, the Batman Family

## POWERS AND ABILITIES

Near genius intellect; brilliant chemist and psychiatrist; crafts fear gas that causes victims to live their worst nightmares.

### KNIGHT TERRORS

Scarecrow is obsessed with fear, taking every opportunity to experiment on his favorite subject, Batman. Using his "fear toxin," he has forced the Dark Knight to relive his tragic past—but Batman triumphs over his inner demons.

**As a boy, Jonathan Crane's** father carried out twisted experiments that tested the emotion of fear. Despite this scary experience, Jonathan followed in his father's footsteps, studying fear as a professor at university. Eventually, his own cruel experiments led to him being fired, which was when he adopted the role of the deadly Scarecrow.

*"I'm the bogeyman."*

Fabric mask with sewn-up mouth

Costume rigged to dispense fear gas

Adopted the name Scarecrow after being compared to one

# THE RIDDLER

## VITAL STATS

**Real Name:** Edward Nygma

**Occupation:** Criminal, former Wayne Enterprises employee

**Height:** 6ft 1in

**Weight:** 183 lbs

**Base:** Gotham City

**Allies:** Arkham Rogues

**Foes:** Batman, the Batman Family

## POWERS AND ABILITIES

Genius-level intellect; expert at creating riddles and death traps; computer and electronics whiz; not above cheating to win a fight.

## RIDDLE ME THIS

Obsessed with riddles from a young age, the Riddler began his campaign of crime by taking Gotham City hostage. Not only did the villain shut off Gotham City's power, but he also would have obliterated the city entirely, if not for Batman's intervention.

**Edward Nygma originally** worked as an advisor for Bruce Wayne's uncle, Philip Kane, at Wayne Enterprises. Even more corrupt than his employer, Nygma met the young Bruce Wayne soon after Bruce's return to Gotham City, and challenged him with a series of riddles. Following a falling out with Kane, Nygma became the Riddler—one of Batman's trickiest opponents.

Bowler hat has replaced his old fedora

Trick cane loaded with remote technology

Trademark green suit

*"It's not a mystery you're dealing with here. It's a riddle."*

# POISON IVY

## VITAL STATS

**Real Name:** Pamela Lillian Isley

**Occupation:** Criminal, eco-terrorist

**Height:** 5ft 8in

**Weight:** 115 lbs

**Base:** Gotham City

**Allies:** Harley Quinn, Clayface, the Justice League United

**Foes:** Batman, the Batman Family, the Birds of Prey

### POWERS AND ABILITIES

Controls and manipulates growth of plants; immune to toxins and poisons; produces pheromones that cause others to fall into her control; poisonous kiss; highly adept at botany and chemistry.

### TANGLED IN IVY

Poison Ivy and Batman have clashed frequently, but they first butted heads when Isley worked briefly for Wayne Enterprises. She was fired for developing a mind-controlling pheromone that Bruce Wayne found immoral.

As a girl, **Pamela Isley** was adept at chemistry and developed a deadly toxin in her mother's garden that she could deliver to her enemies with a kiss. When she was accidentally doused with an experimental plant-based serum during a struggle in her lab, she gained the ability to communicate with nature. She soon set out to exploit that power as the eco-terrorist, Poison Ivy.

*"Are you scared, little mammal?"*

Can "speak" to plants and control them

Highly intelligent, with a mind for chemistry

Body changes with seasons like a true plant

Wears plant-based living costume

97

# TWO-FACE

## VITAL STATS

**Real Name:** Harvey Dent
**Occupation:** Criminal,
former District Attorney
**Height:** 6ft
**Weight:** 182 lbs
**Base:** Gotham City
**Allies:** The Secret Society,
Gilda Dent
**Foes:** Batman, the Batman
Family, Erin McKillen

## POWERS AND ABILITIES

Cunning strategist; expert
knowledge of law and
police procedure; split
personality causes
extreme unpredictability.

### TWO SIDES OF THE SAME COIN
Harvey Dent and his
old friend Bruce Wayne
have become enemies
as Two-Face and
Batman. With a flip
of his special coin,
Two-Face lets luck
dictate his every
decision—good or evil.

**Gotham City's District Attorney,**
Harvey Dent, led a promising life as the
city's golden boy. But when he crossed
Erin McKillen of the organized crime
family known as the McKillen Clan,
his life changed forever. Erin took
revenge upon Harvey and his family.
The trauma of this tragic event
released Harvey's dark side, and he took
on the persona of the criminal Two-Face.

Handsome
features are now
forever marred

Scarred two-
headed coin to
match his face

Wears
two-toned
clothing

> "Chance *trumps* choice *every
> second of every day.*"

# THE JOKER'S DAUGHTER

## VITAL STATS

**Real Name:** Duela Dent
**Occupation:** Criminal, leader of underground cult
**Height:** 5ft 4in
**Weight:** 120 lbs
**Base:** Gotham City
**Allies:** Suicide Squad
**Foes:** Catwoman, Batman, Batgirl

## POWERS AND ABILITIES

Criminal mastermind; uses the Joker's urban legend to her advantage; manic fighter; employs moon-shaped blade for combat.

### CLOWN PRINCESS

The Joker's Daughter gained followers when she took control of an underground tribe in the Nethers. Obsessed with the Joker, she has run afoul of Batman, Catwoman, and Batgirl in her short criminal career.

**Duela was a disturbed** young woman living with her family in the Gotham City suburbs. After her face was scarred during a botched surgery, she fled for the grime and squalor of Gotham City's underground tunnels. There she discovered the Joker's lost skin mask. In a grab for power, she adopted it as her own face, becoming the so-called Joker's Daughter.

*"Hit me like one of your super-villains, Batman!"*

Clad in the Joker's colors: purple and green

Wears the Joker's skin as a mask

Staff often has moon-shaped blade

Shirt design implies the Joker is her father

# BANE

## VITAL STATS

**Real Name:** Unknown
**Occupation:** Criminal
**Height:** 6ft 8in
**Weight:** 350 lbs (425 lbs on Venom)
**Base:** Gotham City
**Allies:** Santa Prisca mercenaries
**Foes:** Batman, the Batman Family, Batwoman

## POWERS AND ABILITIES

Extremely intelligent with an iron-clad will; brilliant strategist; skilled hand-to-hand fighter; enhanced strength, durability, weight, and endurance due to use of super-steroid Venom.

### BREAKING BAT

Bane lives with one goal in mind: to break the Batman. Bane had heard legends of the Dark Knight while in his native country of Santa Prisca, and yearned to conquer the seemingly untamable Gotham City and its dark protector.

**Born in the corrupt nation** of Santa Prisca, the boy who would become Bane grew up in its cruelest prison, Pena Duro, becoming a hardened yet well-read man. The prison doctors injected him with a powerful steroid called Venom. Not only did the steroid work, it gave Bane the strength he needed to escape and set his sights on Gotham City.

*"Only when I'm dead do I intend to rest."*

Always equipped with Venom supply

Venom injected directly into head

Huge exterior can overshadow brilliant mind

Often leads army of Santa Prisca soldiers

# CLAYFACE

ROGUE

## VITAL STATS

**Real Name:** Basil Karlo

**Occupation:** Criminal, former actor

**Height:** Varies

**Weight:** Varies

**Base:** Gotham City

**Allies:** Poison Ivy, the Unknowns, Batwoman

**Foes:** Batman, the Batman Family

## POWERS AND ABILITIES

Made of living clay that can bend and shape to his will; able to impersonate others by taking their exact shape and DNA; highly skilled actor.

## IMPRESSIONABLE

While Clayface has primarily been an enemy of Batman, he briefly joined forces with Batwoman and a team called the Unknowns when he suffered from amnesia. He has since reverted to his criminal ways.

**Basil Karlo was a** famous actor, known primarily for his roles in horror films. However, when replaced as the lead in a movie, he turned to murder. His life began to take a strange path when he injected himself with a formula that altered his body completely, making him a shape-changer made of living clay. He became Clayface, one of Batman's most powerful enemies.

*"...I ain't your daddy's Clayface!"*

When Clayface takes on the forms of others, he now adopts their DNA. He can be anyone by just touching them; anyone but the man he once was.

# RĀ'S AL GHŪL

## VITAL STATS

**Real Name:** Unknown

**Occupation:** International terrorist

**Height:** 6ft 5in

**Weight:** 215 lbs

**Base:** 'Eth Alth'eban

**Allies:** The League of Assassins, Talia al Ghūl.

**Foes:** Batman, Robin, the Batman Family

## POWERS AND ABILITIES

Extremely long-life through his unprecedented access to the anti-aging Lazarus Pits; expert swordsman; highly skilled martial artist and fighter; genius intellect; master strategist.

### HEIR APPARENT

Despite living for hundreds of years due to the Lazarus Pits, Rā's al Ghūl knows that he will die one day. He has tried hard to make Batman take on the role as his successor, but the Dark Knight constantly rejects his offer.

**Legend tells of Rā's al Ghūl** walking the Earth for the last 700 years. He adopted the name "The Demon's Head" after the death of his wife. Prolonging his own life through restorative Lazarus Pits, Rā's has amassed an entire League of Assassins with the goal of destroying the majority of the population in order to shape the world in his cruel image.

> "My League of Assassins will tear this world apart..."

Speaks many different languages

Aging slowed thanks to Lazarus Pits

Ornate gold detailing

Wears regal clothing fit for a ruler

# TALIA AL GHŪL

## VITAL STATS

**Full Name:** Talia al Ghūl
**Occupation:** International terrorist
**Height:** 5ft 8in
**Weight:** 120 lbs
**Base:** Mobile
**Allies:** Rā's al Ghūl, Leviathan, Red Hood, the League of Assassins
**Foes:** Batman, Robin, the Batman Family, Batman, Inc.

## POWERS AND ABILITIES

Access to huge terrorist networks; superb fighter and assassin; extremely intelligent with a mind for strategy; charismatic leader; worked her way into both Batman and Robin's hearts.

### IN THE NAME OF THE FATHER

While she stayed by his side for years, Talia al Ghūl later parted ways with her father. She formed her own terrorist organization called Leviathan, and set out to destroy Batman once and for all.

**Talia al Ghūl** is the daughter of the terrorist Rā's al Ghūl, and grew up learning the evil methods of being an assassin. When she met Batman, the two were instantly attracted to one another and had a short-lived romance that resulted in the birth of their son, Damian Wayne. While leading the criminal organization Leviathan, Talia was shot and presumably killed.

> **"Look into the eye of the gorgon."**

Uses laboratories for immoral experiments

Beauty causes some to drop their guard

Wears expensive regal attire

# THE LEAGUE OF ASSASSINS

ROGUES

## VITAL STATS

**Team Name:** The League of Assassins

**Base:** 'Eth Alth'eban

**Allies:** Rā's al Ghūl, Talia al Ghūl, Red Hood

**Foes:** Batman, the Batman Family, Deathstroke, the Untitled

**Notable Members:** Rā's al Ghūl, Talia al Ghūl, Lady Shiva, Bronze Tiger, Cheshire, December Graystone, Rictus, Dr. Darrk, Red Hood (former), Anya Volkova (former)

### EVE OF DESTRUCTION

Always pursuing immortality, Rā's al Ghūl sent the League of Assassins to Mother Eve, hoping to learn the secret of her de-aging process. Fortunately, Batgirl and the Birds of Prey were on hand to defend their ally.

**Formed by the international** terrorist Rā's al Ghūl, the League of Assassins is an elite and clandestine organization based in the mystical city of 'Eth Alth'eban. The League is usually led by Rā's, whose ultimate goal is to destroy a significant portion of the world's population in order to shape what is left into a world of his choosing.

*"We are the League of Assassins. We are death incarnate."*

Rā's al Ghūl takes a hands-on approach as leader of the League of Assassins. He is very often present during its missions.

# LADY SHIVA

ROGUE

## VITAL STATS

**Real Name:** Sandra Wu-San

**Occupation:** Mercenary

**Height:** 5ft 8in

**Weight:** 115 lbs

**Base:** 'Eth Alth'eban

**Allies:** The League of Assassins, Rā's al Ghūl, Ninja Man-Bats

**Foes:** Batman, Dick Grayson, the Untitled

### POWERS AND ABILITIES

Arguably the world's greatest martial artist; master of many weapons; commands army of Ninja Man-Bats when working with the League of Assassins; brilliant and cunning mind.

### SHIVA THE DESTROYER

When Dick Grayson was Robin, he interrupted a fight between Batman and Lady Shiva. Lady Shiva has the skill to read fighting styles like language, so when she later met Grayson in his Nightwing guise, she instantly recognized him.

Thinks several steps ahead of her opponents

Even her hair is weaponized with a blade

Expert at nearly every type of traditional weapon

**Lady Shiva is considered** one of the world's greatest assassins, and boasts a long history with Batman and his allies. As a member of the League of Assassins, Shiva has worked directly for Rā's al Ghūl, as well as commanded her own missions. Despite working with the League, Lady Shiva is most often found alone, committing one assassination after another.

*"Fear us. Fear me. Lady Shiva!"*

# MR. FREEZE

## VITAL STATS

**Real Name:** Dr. Victor Fries
**Occupation:** Criminal, former scientist
**Height:** 6ft
**Weight:** 190 lbs
**Base:** Gotham City
**Allies:** Starling, Scarecrow, Harley Quinn, Merrymaker, Professor Pyg
**Foes:** Batman, the Batman Family, the Birds of Prey, the Court of Owls

## POWERS AND ABILITIES

Refrigerated suit gives him superhuman strength and endurance; developed quick-freeze technology in the form of freeze guns and grenades; genius-level intellect.

## ICE IN HIS VEINS

With a body temperature of 23 degrees Fahrenheit, Victor Fries was fitted with special goggles to keep his eyes from freezing. He developed a refrigerated exoskeleton and an arsenal of cold weapons to become Mr. Freeze.

**When Victor Fries was** just a boy, his mother died in a frozen lake. As an adult, he took a job at Wayne Enterprises' cryogenics lab, where he focused on freezing bodies. He became obsessed with the frozen body of a woman he'd never met, Nora Fields. When Bruce Wayne closed his division, Fries lashed out, causing a lab accident that transformed him into Mr. Freeze.

> *"You don't understand what you're meddling with, Batman."*

Mr. Freeze is obsessed with Nora Fields and believes they were married before she was frozen. He'll kill anyone that hampers finding her a cure.

# KILLER CROC

## VITAL STATS

**Real Name:** Waylon Jones

**Occupation:** Criminal

**Height:** 6ft 5in

**Weight:** 268 lbs

**Base:** Gotham City

**Allies:** Arsenal, Catwoman

**Foes:** Batman, the Batman Family, Bane

## POWERS AND ABILITIES

Enhanced strength, durability, and endurance due to rare skin condition; excellent fighter with a history of wrestling alligators.

## LURKING IN THE SEWERS

On the surface, Killer Croc can be perceived as simple muscle, but in the sewers he commands respect. Croc knows the underground inside and out, and has even ruled over tribes of vagabonds. He is known to them as King Croc.

**Waylon Jones was raised** by his Aunt Flowers in the poor neighborhood of Crown Point in Gotham City. Born with a skin condition that caused scale growth all over his body, Waylon knew no other life aside from one in a circus sideshow. Frustrated with his low pay and, after biting his employer while in a rage, Jones ventured into a life of crime as Killer Croc.

*"Death by Croc."*

Teeth filed to sharp points

Extremely strong and muscular

Skin tough and difficult to pierce

# CARMINE FALCONE

**ROGUE**

## VITAL STATS

**Full Name:** Carmine Falcone
**Occupation:** Crime boss
**Height:** 6ft 1in
**Weight:** 205 lbs
**Base:** Gotham City
**Allies:** Mayor Sebastian Hady, Jack Forbes, Tiger Shark
**Foes:** Batman, Catwoman, James Gordon, the Penguin

## POWERS AND ABILITIES

Powerful crime boss; highly connected in Gotham City's underworld; amassed wealth through illegal means; intelligent, strategic mind; years of criminal experience.

### ET TU, CATWOMAN?

During Batman's campaign to drive Falcone out of Gotham City, Catwoman lashed out at the crime boss, scarring his face with her claws. Falcone has sought revenge against Catwoman ever since.

**It took the combined efforts** of Batman and James Gordon to run the organized crime boss Carmine "the Roman" Falcone out of Gotham City. So when Falcone returned to the city when Gordon was wrongly imprisoned, it was certainly cause for concern. Carmine's second stay in Gotham City was cut short, however, when he was arrested by the G.C.P.D.'s Jason Bard.

*"This city won't let me lose."*

Carmine Falcone is good at making enemies. He was once abducted by Professor Pyg and his animal-masked gang before Batman saved his life.

# REX "THE LION" CALABRESE

## VITAL STATS

**Full Name:** Rex Calabrese

**Occupation:** Former crime boss

**Height:** 6ft

**Weight:** 265 lbs

**Base:** Gotham City

**Allies:** Catwoman, the Calabrese Crime family

**Foes:** Carmine Falcone, Batman, the Penguin

### POWERS AND ABILITIES

Powerful former crime boss; highly connected in Gotham City's underworld; amassed wealth through illegal means; intelligent, strategic mind; years of criminal experience.

### LUCK OF THE LION

Named "Leo" by fellow inmates, Calabrese has spent the last several years in Blackgate Penitentiary. His former protégé, Carmine Falcone, thought he had killed Calabrese, and had no idea he was hiding in jail.

**Rex "The Lion" Calabrese** was once one of the most powerful underworld figures in Gotham City. His career was thought to be cut short when he was "killed" by a former ally. In reality, Rex was in hiding, and eventually made contact with his daughter, Selina Kyle, to persuade her to take over the family crime business. She agreed, although she harbored many angry feelings toward him.

> *"The cat's outta the bag, so to speak."*

When Catwoman's father first approached her to unite Gotham City's crime families, she lashed out, angry that he had abandoned her.

# ANTHONY ZUCCO

## VITAL STATS

**Full Name:** Anthony Zucco

**Occupation:** Criminal, former mayor's aide

**Height:** 6ft

**Weight:** 240 lbs

**Base:** Chicago

**Ally:** Mayor Wallace Cole

**Foes:** Dick Grayson, Sophia Branch, Prankster, Batman

## POWERS AND ABILITIES

Intelligent strategist; many criminal connections in the Gotham City underworld and in Chicago; personal friend of the mayor of Chicago; uses firearm.

## ACCEPTING RESPONSIBILITY

Tony Zucco attempted to turn his life around in Chicago, assuming the fake name Billy Lester, marrying, and having a child. When Nightwing tracked him down, Zucco finally came clean and admitted his guilt.

**Tony Zucco was** a shakedown artist with plans to make a name for himself. When attempting to gain protection money from Haly's Circus, Zucco threatened C.C. Haly, a crime a young Dick Grayson witnessed. So when Dick's parents were murdered during their trapeze routine, he knew who the culprit was. Dick hunted Zucco, but the criminal faked his own death.

*"...what I did to the Graysons... there's no excuse I can make."*

Tony Zucco did much harm in Gotham City. His daughter, however, distanced herself from him by changing her name to Sonia Branch.

# JOE CHILL

## VITAL STATS

**Full Name:** Joe Chill

**Occupation:** Criminal

**Height:** 5ft 8in

**Weight:** 180 lbs

**Base:** Gotham City

**Allies:** Unknown

**Foes:** Batman, Thomas and Martha Wayne

### POWERS AND ABILITIES

Common street criminal with access to a handgun.

### CHILL OF THE NIGHT

Joe Chill happened upon the Waynes when they were exiting a movie on Gotham City's Park Row. He was startled by Martha Wayne's scream, and shot her and her husband.

**When young Bruce Wayne's** parents were gunned down before his eyes, his life was forever changed. Although he suspected the Court of Owls or some other nefarious organization of being the culprit, he later learned the killer was Joe Chill, after a witness identified the murderer. Bruce tracked Chill to his apartment, to discover not a mastermind, but a petty criminal.

*"I didn't mean to."*

When Bruce Wayne finally tracked down Chill, he planned to kill him. However, Bruce couldn't pull the trigger, and instead let the sad man live.

# THE COURT OF OWLS

## VITAL STATS

**Team Name:** The Court of Owls

**Base:** Gotham City

**Allies:** Army of Talons and fellow secret Owl members

**Foes:** Batman, Bane, Talon (Calvin Rose), Lincoln March

**Notable Past Members:** Benjamin Orchard, John Wycliffe, Maria Powers, Joseph Powers, Sebastian Clark, Lincoln March

### GRIPPED BY TALONS
Batman mistakenly suspected the Court of Owls was behind his parents' murder. He first encountered the Court when he was trapped in their labyrinth beneath Gotham City, and he barely managed to escape.

**A cult as old as Gotham City** itself, the Court of Owls is a secret society of the most nefarious order. Clandestinely controlling politics and the evolution of the city from behind closed doors, the Court employs an elite army of Talons —loyal assassins who murder their enemies from the shadows. Batman stopped a troubling resurgence, but the Court is still alive in Gotham City.

*"...Beware the Court of Owls, that watches all the time..."*

Members wear owl masks to hide identities

Children brainwashed at young age

Order members are typically society's richest

# TALON

ROGUE

## VITAL STATS

**Real Name:** William Cobb

**Occupation:** Assassin for the Court of Owls

**Height:** 6ft 3in

**Weight:** 220 lbs

**Base:** Gotham City

**Allies:** The Court of Owls

**Foes:** Batman, Dick Grayson, the Batman Family

### POWERS AND ABILITIES

Expertly trained assassin; natural fighter and trained martial artist; superb at knife throwing; has healing ability and can be resurrected from the dead; long-lived and experienced.

## CAPE VS. CLAW

When Bruce Wayne was targeted by Talon, Batman began investigating the Court of Owls. This led him to discover the Court's labyrinth, where he was forced to combat Cobb and just barely triumphed over him to escape.

**William Cobb, one of** the Court of Owls's finest Talon assassins, is the great-grandfather of Dick Grayson. Growing up poor on the streets of Gotham City in the early 1900s, Cobb was recruited into Haly's Circus where he became an expert knife handler. Cobb soon became a Talon for the Court of Owls, later offering his "gray son" to Haly's Circus for training.

> *"Bruce Wayne. The Court of Owls has sentenced you to die."*

Uses owls and owl imagery to threaten

Wears owl-like enhanced goggles

Expert knife thrower

Each Talon wears a different uniform

# LINCOLN MARCH

## VITAL STATS

**Real Name:** Unknown
**Occupation:** Criminal
**Height:** 6ft 4in
**Weight:** 230 lbs
**Base:** Gotham City
**Ally:** Cluemaster
**Foes:** Batman, the Court
of Owls, the Batman Family

## POWERS AND ABILITIES

Skilled combatant;
advanced armored
Talon suit allows for
flight, enhanced
strength, and durability;
suit is fitted with hi-tech
devices; brilliant strategist
with powerful underworld
connections; healing
abilities; can be resurrected
from the dead.

### MARCH ON GOTHAM CITY

After dying and then being
regenerated by the Court of
Owls, Lincoln March adopted
an owl costume and battled
Batman. March wanted to
destroy the Dark Knight,
but he also killed fellow Owls
in order to steal their riches.

**Despite his claims** to the contrary,
the true origin of Lincoln March
remains a mystery. He insists he is
Thomas Wayne, Jr., Bruce Wayne's
younger brother who was believed to
have died in a car crash. According to
March, he was placed in Willowwood
Home for Children by his parents after
Martha Wayne's car accident, and
was forgotten after their death.

*"Brother to brother...
owl to bat!"*

Is taller than
his "brother"
Batman

Has taken
Owls's healing
serum to be
resurrected

Often trades
civilian clothes
for Talon suit

ROGUE

## VITAL STATS

**Real Name:** Etienne Guiborg

**Occupation:** Auctioneer of illegal goods

**Height:** 5ft 6in

**Weight:** 120 lbs

**Base:** Gotham City

**Ally:** Mirror House

**Foes:** Dick Grayson, Batman

## POWERS AND ABILITIES

Connections to a large criminal network able to secure various illegal and contraband items for him; extremely intelligent and manipulative; uses Venom and an outdated Man-Bat formula to turn into a large and super-strong bat-like creature.

### A REAL GAS AT PARTIES

To ensure his auctions are exclusive and anonymous, the Dealer fills the room with a poisonous gas and requires all the participants to hide their identities behind life-saving gas masks.

**Dick Grayson first** became aware of the Dealer when he briefly took over the role of Batman in Bruce Wayne's absence. Discovering evidence missing from the G.C.P.D., Batman followed a trail to locate a secret society called "Mirror House." Entering one of their auctions under a fake name, Grayson was discovered and nearly killed by the Dealer's people before escaping.

*"There you have it—the market has spoken!"*

The Dealer ran into Nightwing when he attempted to sell a circus costume worn by John Grayson that had been vandalized by the Joker.

# MAN-BAT

## VITAL STATS

**Real Name:** Dr. Kirk Langstrom

**Occupation:** Scientist and science teacher, acting head of S.H.A.D.E. Security

**Height:** 6ft 1in

**Weight:** 201 lbs

**Base:** Gotham City

**Allies:** Gotham Academy, S.H.A.D.E., the Outlaws

**Foes:** Batman, Bat-Queen, the Batman Family

## POWERS AND ABILITIES

Serum transforms him into a monstrous Man-Bat with enhanced strength, speed, agility, and endurance, with capability of flight; genius-level intellect.

## BAT VS. MAN

While Kirk's savagery as Man-Bat has put him at odds with Batman, he has recently found a way to control his transformations, now taking jobs at the clandestine operation S.H.A.D.E., as well as at Gotham Academy.

**Dr. Kirk Langstrom** is a noble scientist who wanted to find a cure for the deaf. He developed the Langstrom Atavistic Gene Recall Serum, but unfortunately it transformed its victims into hideous humanoid bat creatures. When a sample of the serum was stolen and unleashed on Gotham City, Kirk injected himself with an anti-virus. This cured the innocents but left Kirk as the sole remaining Man-Bat.

*"I had to become the creature."*

Combining several doses of his serum with a serum created by his wife, Langstrom can change into Man-Bat with only a thought.

## VITAL STATS

**Real Name:** Francine Langstrom (Felicity Lee)

**Occupation:** Criminal and corporate spy

**Height:** 5ft 11in

**Weight:** 169 lbs

**Base:** Gotham City

**Ally:** The Wrath

**Foes:** Man-Bat, Batman, G.C.P.D.

## POWERS AND ABILITIES

Serum transforms her into a monstrous She-Bat with enhanced strength, speed, agility, and endurance, with capability of flight; controls army of piranha-like bats; manipulative and ruthless.

## QUEEN OF THE NIGHT

As the villain Bat-Queen, Francine Langstrom's main opposition was her husband, Kirk. Angered that his wife had married him under false pretenses, Kirk wanted nothing more than to put an end to his wife's wicked ways.

**The wife of Dr. Kirk Langstrom,** who would become Man-Bat, Francine Langstrom's real name is Felicity Lee. A spy tasked with keeping an eye on Kirk's scientific work for her boss, E.D. Caldwell, Francine wanted to help her employer create a biological weapon from Kirk's findings. Creating her own imperfect Man-Bat formula, Francine became the highly unstable Bat-Queen.

High frequency sounds leave her disorientated

Sharpened claws can easily tear through flesh

Stronger than Man-Bat himself

*"...I am—the Bat-Queen! Screeeee!"*

# BRONZE TIGER

## VITAL STATS

**Real Name:** Ben Turner
**Occupation:** Mercenary
**Height:** 5ft 11in
**Weight:** 196 lbs
**Base:** 'Eth Alth'æban
**Allies:** Rā's al Ghūl, the
League of Assassins,
Deathstroke
**Foes:** The Untitled, Batman

## POWERS AND ABILITIES

One of the world's best
martial artists; proficient
in a variety of fighting styles
and weapons; contacts in
the espionage and criminal
worlds; access to the League
of Assassins's assets; able
to shift into animalistic tiger
form; often wears tiger-
themed armor into battle.

### TIGER STYLE

An old drinking buddy
of Deathstroke's,
the Bronze Tiger
nevertheless agreed
to kill his friend when
his mind was being
manipulated. Despite
working directly with
fellow assassin Lady
Shiva on this mission,
the Tiger was
unsuccessful.

**Ben Turner is a ranking** member
of the clandestine mercenary group,
the League of Assassins. His ability
to transform into a tiger is a useful
asset, although it comes at a price.
When the vigilante Red Hood was
recruited to briefly lead the group, the
Bronze Tiger welcomed him. While it
is known that he is Deathstroke's old
friend, his past remains a mystery.

*"Do yourself a favor and yield."*

The Bronze Tiger has a talisman that "burns away"
at his soul every time he transforms into a tiger.
Nonetheless, he often finds it useful in a fight.

# DR. DARRK

## VITAL STATS

**Real Name:** Dr. Ebenezer Darcel
**Occupation:** Criminal
**Height:** 7ft 4in
**Weight:** 386 lbs
**Base:** Mobile
**Allies:** The League of Assassins, Rā's al Ghūl
**Foes:** Batman, Talon, Lord Death Man

## POWERS AND ABILITIES

Forced to live in a cybernetic body that allows him superhuman strength, endurance, and durability; highly intelligent; access to the assets of the League of Assassins.

### LORDING OVER DEATH

As Rā's al Ghūl's employee, the now cybernetically-enhanced Dr. Darrk attempted to mine the secret of Lord Death Man's immortality by extracting the so-called Shelley Formula from his very blood.

**When Batman first met** Talia al Ghūl, the two became allies when he rescued her from the clutches of Dr. Darrk. While Batman had no idea that Talia's father, Rā's al Ghūl, was the head of the notorious League of Assassins, and that Dr. Darrk had fallen out with his employer, Batman took Talia's side, and comforted her when it appeared she had shot and killed Dr. Darrk.

*"I've prepared a welcome for our would-be nemesis, our dark pursuer."*

Dr. Darrk did not die at Talia's hands. Resurfacing as a member of the League of Assassins, he later attempted to best Batman using hallucinogenic gas.

# DOLLMAKER

## VITAL STATS

**Real Name:** Barton Mathis

**Occupation:** Criminal

**Height:** 6ft 1in

**Weight:** 169 lbs

**Base:** Gotham City

**Allies:** The Joker, the Joker's Daughter, Dollhouse

**Foes:** Batman, the Batman Family, James Gordon

## POWERS AND ABILITIES

Skilled surgeon capable of stitching living and dead bodies together to form gruesome "dolls"; intelligent yet twisted mind.

### FAMILY MAN

The Dollmaker has passed on his gruesome pastime to his family members, including his son Bentley and his associates Jack-in-the-Box and Sampson. He also has a daughter called Dollhouse, who once battled Catwoman.

**The son of serial killer** Wesley Mathis, Barton Mathis watched his father get shot down by James Gordon. Seeking revenge, and now calling himself the Dollmaker, he kidnapped the police commissioner, only to have Batman interrupt his scheme. Dollmaker created his most infamous work of "art" when he cut skin from the Joker's face.

*"This will only hurt—a lot."*

Wears mask made from victims' skin

Gifted surgeon with great medical expertise

## VITAL STATS

**Real Name:** Unknown
**Occupation:** Criminal
**Height:** 5ft 7in
**Weight:** 208 lbs
**Base:** Gotham City
**Allies:** Emperor Blackgate, Mr. Combustible, Imperceptible Man, Mr. Toxic
**Foes:** Batman, the Batman Family, G.C.P.D.

### POWERS AND ABILITIES

Has extensive ties in the political and criminal world; wealthy, and hires others to do his dirty work for him.

### THE LONG GAME

Mr. Mosaic talks a big game, but when confronted with physical danger, he backs down from his larger-than-life persona quite quickly. Instead, he bides his time and looks for an opportunity for revenge down the line.

**Little is known** about how Mr. Mosaic rose to power in Gotham City's underworld, or even how he developed his bizarre skin condition. What is known, however, is that he is very influential in the criminal scene, and has worked with Emperor Blackgate. He raided the docks for the gang leader while the rest of Gotham City was busy dealing with Blackgate's Man-Bat virus.

*"Think a hitchhiker with a face like this can get a ride?"*

Mr. Mosaic was one of the criminals freed by Bane when the villain organized a massive breakout at Blackgate Penitentiary.

# HUGO STRANGE

## VITAL STATS

**Full Name:** Dr. Hugo Strange

**Occupation:** Psychiatrist, school counselor, criminal

**Height:** 5ft 10½in

**Weight:** 170 lbs

**Base:** Gotham City

**Allies:** Eli Strange, Crazy Quilt, Dr. Death

**Foes:** Batman, the Batman Family

## POWERS AND ABILITIES

Extremely persuasive and manipulative; expert scientist known for his unorthodox experiments; well connected in the criminal underground and Super Hero community; highly intelligent; in excellent physical condition.

## THE DOCTOR IS IN

A bit of a psychiatrist to the stars when not plotting the downfall of Batman, Hugo Strange has been known to give personal counsel to Arsenal, Red Hood's partner and longtime Outlaws teammate.

**It has been difficult** for Batman to prove the corrupt nature of Professor Hugo Strange. Despite their frequent clashes, Hugo keeps reemerging in the Dark Knight's life in various legitimate positions. One of the infamous Doctors Three alongside Crazy Quilt and Dr. Death, Hugo is now a counselor at Gotham Academy, as if his past crimes never occurred.

*"I'll keep our talks a secret. I am here to help you."*

Strange takes pride in manipulating the minds of others for his own selfish gain, especially the aspiring young students at Gotham Academy.

## VITAL STATS

**Full Name:** Victor Zsasz

**Occupation:** Criminal

**Height:** 5ft 8in

**Weight:** 150 lbs

**Base:** Gotham City

**Ally:** Emperor Blackgate

**Foes:** Batman, the Penguin, Merrymaker

### POWERS AND ABILITIES
Deadly efficient murderer; excellent physical condition; mentally unstable and obsessed with murder; usually prefers using blades or knives.

### DEATH TALLY
One of Gotham City's most dangerous and psychotic villains, Mr. Zsasz likes to keep a tally of his kills. For every person he murders, he carves a notch in his own flesh to remember them by.

**Victor Zsasz has an** addictive personality, and was therefore an easy mark when he gambled in the Penguin's Iceberg Casino. The heir to Zsasz Industries, Victor lost all his money thanks to the Penguin encouraging his love of gambling. Victor's mind snapped, and he embarked on a killing spree that continues to this day, despite Batman's efforts to stop him.

*"The bird-man. This was all his doing. He gave me the knife."*

While he usually prefers to work alone, Zsasz has been the willing pawn of Emperor Blackgate in the past, helping to spread the Man-Bat virus.

# THE CRIME SYNDICATE

## VITAL STATS

**Group Name:** The Crime Syndicate

**Base:** Happy Harbor, Rhode Island

**Allies:** The Secret Society

**Foes:** The Justice League, Mazahs, Lex Luthor, the Justice League of America

**Members:**
Owlman, Ultraman, Superwoman, Power Ring (deceased), Johnny Quick (deceased), Atomica (deceased), Sea King (deceased), Deathstorm (deceased), Grid (deceased)

### INJUSTICE FOR ALL

The Crime Syndicate are the evil equivalent of the Justice League, headed by three notorious super-villains: Ultraman is the dark mirror to Superman; Superwoman is the corrupted version of Wonder Woman, and Owlman is Earth-Three's evil Batman.

**In the parallel dimension** of Earth-Three, evil overshadows good. There, the Crime Syndicate served as an evil Justice League of sorts. When the Crime Syndicate fled to the Justice League's dimension, they banished the Justice League to a prison inside the matrix of the hero Firestorm. Meanwhile, they caused a planet-wide blackout and declared themselves rulers of the world.

*"This world is ours."*

Despite uniting the world's super-villains, the Crime Syndicate finally fell when Batman and a team of villains invaded the Syndicate's headquarters.

# SIGNALMAN

## VITAL STATS

**Real Name:** Phil Cobb

**Occupation:** Criminal

**Height:** 6ft 2in

**Weight:** 200 lbs

**Base:** Gotham City

**Allies:** Blockbuster, the Secret Society, Firefly, Cluemaster, Lock-Up

**Foes:** Batman, the Batman Family

## POWERS AND ABILITIES

Employs a variety of signal-themed gadgets; very intelligent, with strong computer hacking skills; keeps himself in excellent physical condition; cultivates connections with many minor criminals.

### ANSWERING THE SIGNAL

The Signalman seems to join any club that will have him as a member, so it made complete sense when he was an early supporter of the villain Outsider and a member of the nefarious Secret Society.

**Small-time criminal Phil Cobb** decided to up his game when he reached Gotham City after seeing the Bat-Signal shining over the skyline. He opted for the identity of Signalman, and his sign-themed robberies soon drew Batman's attention. Involved in Cluemaster and Lincoln March's plan to kill the Dark Knight, he also played a major role in the Secret Society.

*"In this town, you learn not to assume anything."*

One of Signalman's greatest strengths is his ability to hack into a city's traffic system, controlling the traffic lights as he sees fit.

# BLOCKBUSTER

## VITAL STATS

**Real Name:** Mark Desmond
**Occupation:** Criminal
**Height:** 8ft
**Weight:** 825 lbs
**Base:** Gotham City
**Allies:** The Secret Society, the Fist of Cain, Roland Desmond
**Foes:** Batman, Hawkman, the Batman Family, Superman

## POWERS AND ABILITIES

Superhuman strength, durability, and endurance; almost completely incapable of thought; prone to fits of rage.

## BATTLE OF THE BLOCKBUSTERS

When Blockbuster returned to his enormous form, he fought another transformed patient, Professor Ziegler. However, after defeat at Blockbuster's hands, Ziegler returned to his normal human state.

**Chemist Mark Desmond** was working on a treatment that would stop violent behavior. However, he was accidentally transformed into a raging behemoth called Blockbuster. After battles with Batman, Robin, and Superman, he found himself at the Rest Haven medical facility —human again and being treated for dementia. But soon, steroid treatments restored his monstrous Blockbuster form.

*"I am Blockbuster— and I crush all!"*

Blockbuster later joined the infamous Secret Society where his brute strength is a powerful weapon in the clandestine group's arsenal.

# COPPERHEAD

## VITAL STATS

**Real Name:** Unknown
**Occupation:** Criminal
**Height:** 6ft 2in
**Weight:** 190 lbs
**Base:** Mobile ·
**Allies:** The Secret Society, Knightfall
**Foes:** The Birds of Prey, Batman, Catwoman, Deathstroke

## POWERS AND ABILITIES

Expert contortionist able to move through small spaces; snake-like ability to squeeze opponents; enhanced flexibility, durability, and endurance; possesses sharp fangs.

### TWO AGAINST ONE

Copperhead once took on Black Canary above the streets of Baltimore. As they battled near an electronic billboard, the Justice League made the billboard flash a bright white light to momentarily blind the snake and help Black Canary win.

**An old foe of Batman's,** the serpentine villain Copperhead joined the Secret Society after learning that they had a way to get villains out of trouble. Unlike other Secret Society members, however, he wanted nothing more than to attack Batman head on. This attitude led to his downfall when he and several other Secret Society members made their attack.

*"It's easier if you don't fight."*

Taking on the Justice League proved unwise. Copperhead lost a fight with Black Canary, and was then killed by Deathstroke.

# THE MAD HATTER

**ROGUE**

## VITAL STATS

**Real Name:** Jervis Tetch

**Occupation:** Criminal

**Height:** 4ft 8in

**Weight:** 149 lbs

**Base:** Gotham City

**Allies:** Tweedledee, Tweedledum

**Foes:** Batman, Red Robin, Bluebird, Black Mask, Anarky

## POWERS AND ABILITIES

Extremely intelligent; brilliant inventor and technician; uses drugged teas to enhance his own physical abilities; fanatically obsessed with Lewis Carroll's stories and poems; creations let him control the minds of others.

### BATTLE OF THE MINDS

The Mad Hatter drinks a variety of drugged teas to give himself an advantage in a fight. Depending on the mixture, his teas can give him heightened pain tolerance or superhuman strength.

**Obsessed with hats** and Lewis Carroll's classic *Alice in Wonderland* stories, a young Jervis Tetch fell in love with his classmate, Alice. When she spurned him, he used testosterone enhancers to help his body grow, but instead developed violent tendencies. Years later, as the Mad Hatter, he uses his gift for invention to ensure that no one will ever reject him again.

Hat contains mind control technology

Often quotes Carroll during encounters

Attire based on Lewis Carroll's Mad Hatter

*"No one gets between me and my beloved!"*

## VITAL STATS

**Real Name:** Dr. Thomas Elliot

**Occupation:** Criminal, Surgeon

**Height:** 6ft 3in

**Weight:** 220 lbs

**Base:** Gotham City

**Allies:** Jason Bard, Architect, the Riddler

**Foes:** Batman, Julia and Alfred Pennyworth

## POWERS AND ABILITIES

Gifted surgeon; brilliant strategist; strong connections to criminal underworld; knows Batman's secret identity; athletic; trained in hand-to-hand combat; highly efficient with firearms.

### FRIENDLY FIRE

Hush has always envied Bruce Wayne, and wanted to be exactly like him. After learning that Bruce Wayne is really Batman, Hush's resolve to destroy Wayne's life became even stronger, often lashing out at those close to him.

**Tommy Elliot was** Bruce Wayne's childhood best friend. After Bruce's parents died, the disturbed Tommy wanted to be an orphan too. As a teenager, Tommy began to imitate Bruce Wayne even more, causing a falling out between the former friends. No longer under Bruce's good influence, Tommy began on a downward spiral, becoming the villain Hush.

*"I'm just like you, Bruce. I'm just like you."*

Wrapped face in bandages after scarring himself

Utility Belt similar to the Dark Knight's

Can operate firearm with either hand

# THE SECRET SOCIETY

## VITAL STATS

**Group Name:** The Secret Society

**Base:** Mobile

**Allies:** The Crime Syndicate

**Foes:** The Justice League, The Justice League of America

**Notable Members:** Outsider (deceased), Scarecrow, Professor Ivo, Copperhead (deceased), Amazo, Dr. Psycho, Multiplex, Blockbuster, Signalman, Shaggy Man

### SOCIETY OF SIN

To form his Secret Society, the Outsider gathered together some of the most nefarious faces from Batman's Rogues Gallery like Copperhead, Signalman, and Blockbuster, as well as enemies of the Justice League, like the android Amazo.

**The evil Crime Syndicate** of Earth-Three wanted to destroy its heroic counterpart, the Justice League. Syndicate member Owlman sent his butler, the Outsider, into the Justice League's world on a covert mission. The Outsider gathered the Justice League's enemies into a Secret Society of super-villains, paving the way for the arrival of the Syndicate.

The Outsider is a villainous Earth-Three version of Alfred. He uses a mystical device called Pandora's Box to create a gateway into another dimension.

> *"...as you say on your world... the butler did it."*

# DARKSEID

## VITAL STATS

**Real Name:** Uxas

**Occupation:** Ruler of Apokolips

**Height:** 8ft 9in

**Weight:** 1,815 lbs

**Base:** Apokolips

**Allies:** Desaad, Kalibak, Granny Goodness, Parademons

**Foes:** The Justice League, Batman, Superman, Highfather, Orion

## POWERS AND ABILITIES

Omega Effect eye beams can kill, resurrect, harm, or send victims hurtling through time; superhuman strength and endurance; commands armies of Parademons, elite soldiers, and a planet of minions.

### GOD AMONG MEN

Darkseid had conquered many worlds before, including Earth-Two, a parallel dimension to the Earth of the Justice League. So when the League chased him off their planet, he swore revenge.

**The planet Apokolips** has been at war with its neighboring world New Genesis for years. Darkseid is the ruler of Apokolips and wants nothing less than to achieve mastery over death and rule the universe. To that end, he has clashed with the Justice League and Batman, when the Dark Knight traveled to Apokolips to rescue the body of the temporarily dead Damian Wayne.

Eyes produce devastating Omega Beams

Stone-like body can overpower even Superman

Towers over members of the Justice League

*"You came a long way to die."*

# SUICIDE SQUAD

## VITAL STATS

**Team Name:** Task Force X, Suicide Squad

**Base:** Belle Reve Penitentiary

**Allies:** Amanda Waller, Vic Sage, James Gordon, Jr.

**Foes:** Deathstroke, Basilisk, The League

**Members:** Deadshot, Harley Quinn, Captain Boomerang, Reverse-Flash, Parasite, Black Manta, King Shark (former), the Joker's Daughter (former), Cheetah (former), Savant (former), Unknown Soldier (former), Iceberg (former), Crowbar (former), El Diablo (former), Light (former), Lime (deceased), Voltaic (deceased), Yo-Yo (deceased), Black Spider (traitor), Deathstroke (traitor)

## DEADLY DISAGREEMENTS

Keeping the Squad in line during missions often proves difficult. The Joker's Daughter and Harley Quinn don't see eye to eye and Deathstroke betrayed the team to the Russians.

**Task Force X is** a secret team, run by Amanda Waller for the US government. Made up of convicted criminals in super-villain costumes, the task force cannot be linked to the government. The roster constantly changes, as different criminals are chosen for their particular sets of skills. The team's nickname—Suicide Squad—reflects the deadly nature of its missions.

*"I want to use prisoners with nothing to lose and everything to gain."*

The Squad is kept in line by explosives implanted at the base of their necks. If they try to escape or change the mission, Waller can detonate them.

# DEADSHOT

## VITAL STATS

**Real Name:** Floyd Lawton

**Occupation:** Mercenary

**Height:** 6ft 1in

**Weight:** 193 lbs

**Base:** Belle Reve Penitentiary

**Allies:** Suicide Squad, Amanda Waller, Harley Quinn

**Foes:** Batman, Deathstroke

### POWERS AND ABILITIES

One of the best marksmen on the planet; armed with wrist cannons and an eye sight in his mask; wears armored suit; adept at using nearly all types of firearms; efficient hand-to-hand combatant; eyesight can see various light spectrums.

### FIRING SQUAD

As a member of the Suicide Squad, it seems as though Deadshot has found purpose in his life. He views some people—like his boss Amanda Waller—as a gun, and himself as a bullet, waiting to be fired.

**Floyd Lawton was a** poor boy growing up in the slums of Gotham City. One day, bullets from a nearby shooting came through the wall of his home and killed his family. That day, Lawton swore revenge and taught himself to shoot. He finally found and shot the men responsible, later finding employment with their boss as a sharpshooter.

Helmet protects against enemy fire

Loves guns, large and small

Eye sight synced with wrist guns

Carries weapons and plenty of ammunition

*"I never miss."*

# DEATHSTROKE

## VITAL STATS

**Real Name:** Slade Wilson
**Occupation:** Mercenary
**Height:** 6ft 4in
**Weight:** 225 lbs
**Base:** Mobile
**Allies:** Suicide Squad, Rose Wilson, Bronze Tiger, Team 7
**Foes:** Batman, Dick Grayson, the Teen Titans

## POWERS AND ABILITIES

Highly trained hand-to-hand combatant; enhanced senses, speed, agility, endurance, and strength; recently returned to a more youthful age; skilled in variety of weapons and firearms; brilliant strategist; connections in criminal underground, military, and government agencies.

### CLASHING WITH DEATH

A gun for hire, Deathstroke is billed as one of the world's best assassins. He has fought many fearsome opponents, from Batman and Harley Quinn to Wonder Woman and Lobo, managing to survive every fight.

**Young Slade Wilson lied** about his age in order to enlist in the army when he was only 16. He advanced quickly through the ranks, and soon joined the special ops group, Team 7. Slade was later the subject of a government experiment that made him into a super-soldier. He began life as an assassin and mercenary for hire: Deathstroke, the Terminator.

*"Smiling? You like pain, Batman?"*

Prefers to use swords and firearms

Wears armored suit in combat

Has worn several costumes over the years

Talented marksman

Carries multiple weapons at all times

# CALENDAR MAN

## VITAL STATS

**Real Name:** Julian Day
**Occupation:** Criminal
**Height:** 6ft 11in
**Weight:** 290 lbs
**Base:** Gotham City
**Ally:** The Squid
**Foe:** Batman

## POWERS AND ABILITIES

Bulky and muscular;
experienced brawler;
obsessed with holidays,
days of the week, and
the calendar.

### MARKING THE CALENDAR

When Batman met Aden Day, the boy
was not being treated well. Batman
donned his often-used criminal disguise
as "Matches" Malone, and hit Julian
Day's head against some tiles, creating
a calendar-like scar on the villain's face.

**Julian Day was a single** father with
a young son, Aden. In order to make
ends meet, he took work as a hired
thug for the crime boss known as
the Squid. Julian was an excellent
enforcer, but he was a terrible father.
When Batman learned that Aden
was not being looked after well
enough, he confronted Julian
and placed Aden in a good home.

Scarred face
resembles a
calendar

Extremely
strong and
muscular

> *"Calendar...get...
> a...calendar..."*

## VITAL STATS

**Real Name:** Thomas Blake
**Occupation:** Bounty hunter
**Height:** 6ft
**Weight:** 179 lbs
**Base:** Gotham City
**Allies:** The Secret Six
**Foes:** Batman, the Riddler

### POWERS AND ABILITIES

Expert hand-to-hand combatant; feels oneness with big cats and is never harmed by them; handsome, with natural charisma and animal magnetism; extremely fit and agile; excellent senses; ferocious temperament.

### FELINE SENSES

Once, Catman was simply minding his own business at a bar in New Mexico when he was kidnapped by the Riddler's men. Despite his captors telling him they worked for the Bureau of Alcohol, Tobacco, and Firearms, Catman sniffed them out as imposters.

**A bounty hunter who** was kidnapped by the Riddler, Thomas Blake was held captive with only a pet kitten to keep him sane. After a year, he was set free until he was captured again, this time with five other criminals: the Riddler had a vendetta against the six for ruining the night of his marriage proposal. However, Blake and the others escaped, forming the Secret Six.

*"We're not the good guys."*

Catman befriended Secret Six member, Big Shot, not realizing that Big Shot was Ralph Dibny, a man taking orders from the Six's enemy, the Riddler.

# CAVALIER

## VITAL STATS

**Real Name:** Mortimer Drake

**Occupation:** Criminal

**Height:** 6ft 1in

**Weight:** 182 lbs

**Base:** Gotham City

**Allies:** Arkham Asylum Inmates

**Foes:** Batman, the Batman Family, Batwoman

## POWERS AND ABILITIES

Expert swordsman known to use electrified rapier; proficient with firearms; witty; adept strategist; costume armed with unexpected weapons; adept hand-to-hand combatant.

### ESCAPE ARTIST
Despite being defeated by the Dark Knight on several occasions, Cavalier is quick to raise his rapier against Batman given the chance, participating in two recent Arkham Asylum breakouts.

**An early foe of** Batman's, Mortimer Drake adopted the name and mantle of the Cavalier after his love of antiques inspired him to rob museums for the finest collectibles known to man. Despite being confined to Arkham Asylum by Batman, Cavalier escaped during a breakout, but luckily, Batwoman was on hand to take the villain down yet again.

Smiles in the face of adversity

Often openly challenges Batman to a duel

Costume similar to those of the Three Musketeers

*"Methinks a palpable and bloody hit—"*

## VITAL STATS

**Real Name:** Dr. Paul Dekker

**Occupation:** Scientist

**Height:** 5ft 11in

**Weight:** 172 lbs

**Base:** Gotham City

**Allies:** Philip Kane, Dr. Death, Hugo Strange, the Joker

**Foe:** Batman

### POWERS AND ABILITIES

Unparalleled genius who created a way for cells to become new again; severely mentally unhinged; extremely knowledgeable in history; obsessed with the chemical compound Dionesium; carries and uses a firearm.

### A STITCH IN CRIME

Paul Dekker was born in the Narrows to a poor family of artists who perished due to a broken gas pipe. A genius, Dekker invented an amazing medical process called "the healing stitch," but his mind later slipped into insanity.

When **Bruce Wayne's uncle**, Philip Kane, ran Wayne Enterprises, he hired the notorious Doctors Three: Dr. Karl Helfern, who worked in bone; Professor Hugo Strange, neural matter expert; and Dr. Paul Dekker, who worked in soft tissue. Like his partners, Dekker's life deteriorated, and he became an Arkham Asylum inmate after doing terrible things in order to meet Batman.

> *"Doesn't feel like a Batman story anymore, does it?"*

Crazy Quilt used his incredible scientific skills to help the Joker develop a virus, which the Joker later released on Gotham City.

# CLUEMASTER

## VITAL STATS

**Real Name:** Arthur Brown

**Occupation:** Criminal, former game show host

**Height:** 5ft 11in

**Weight:** 169 lbs

**Base:** Gotham City

**Allies:** Lock-Up, Signalman, Firefly, Lincoln March

**Foes:** Spoiler, Batman, the Batman Family

## POWERS AND ABILITIES

Clever strategist; trivia expert obsessed with clues; wears protective suit and hi-tech goggles; armed with weaponized capsules called plasti-pellets; connections to powerful figures in Gotham City underworld.

### CLUELESS

Teaming with Lincoln March and several supposedly "D-list" villains, Cluemaster set out to rid Gotham City of Batman. Unfortunately, he didn't count on his own daughter, Spoiler, discovering one of his late night meetings with his accomplices.

**The host of "Quizbowl,"** a trivia game show, Arthur Brown lost his job after yelling at a contestant. Upset that the "intellectually inferior" were wealthy while he was poor, he embarked on a life of crime as the Cluemaster. He attempted to prove his superiority over his robbery victims by leaving clues behind, clues that eventually led to his capture by Batman.

*"I have taken everything from you, piece by piece."*

Cluemaster used his ability to fly under the radar and plot the near-death of Batman, until he was seemingly killed by Lincoln March.

# PARAGON

## VITAL STATS

**Real Name:** Unknown
**Occupation:** Criminal cult leader
**Height:** 6ft
**Weight:** 194 lbs
**Base:** Gotham City
**Allies:** Republic of Tomorrow
**Foes:** Dick Grayson, G.C.P.D.

## POWERS AND ABILITIES

Expert at use of duel energy blades with rotating plasma core; leads cult of similarly armored and weaponized extremists; genius-level intellect and thermodynamics expert; keen manipulator.

### HERE TODAY, PARAGON TOMORROW

Nightwing discovered that Paragon had framed him for the murder of two of the Republic of Tomorrow's members. He confronted the villain and eventually turned him over to police custody.

**Paragon is the leader** of a fanatical cult known as the Republic of Tomorrow. As a teenager, he studied thermodynamics and was able to build a working reactor at just 16 years old. After developing a rotating plasma core to power energy blades, he adopted the name Paragon and began leading a group of armed cultists into what he viewed as a better tomorrow.

Enhanced sight through lenses

Wears armored body suit

Paragon's symbol, worn by all followers

Designed energy blades himself

*"The revolution, Nightwing... begins with your death!"*

# PRANKSTER

## VITAL STATS

**Real Name:** Oswald Loomis

**Occupation:** Criminal

**Height:** 5ft 10in

**Weight:** 170 lbs

**Base:** Chicago

**Ally:** Cluemaster

**Foes:** Dick Grayson, Mayor Wallace Cole, Batman

## POWERS AND ABILITIES

Genius-level computer hacker; master manipulator with dozens of followers; access to funds that allow for elaborate death traps; cunning, with a mind for revenge.

### PULLING THE PRANK

When temporarily living in Chicago, Nightwing took on the Prankster and narrowly avoided dying in the villain's death traps. The Prankster was later defeated by Tony Zucco, the man who killed Nightwing's parents.

Mask similar to his childhood costume

Loves to play cunning mind games

**When Oswald Loomis** was a boy, his father was killed on Halloween night—a crime for which the criminal William Cole was jailed. Loomis was wearing a Halloween mask that night, which he mailed to Cole, as a promise of revenge. He eventually got his payback when he framed William Cole's brother, Wallace, the mayor of Chicago, for embezzlement.

*"...where's the prank?"*

## VITAL STATS

**Real Name:** Aaron Helzinger

**Occupation:** Criminal

**Height:** 7ft 5in

**Weight:** 343 lbs

**Base:** Gotham City

**Ally:** Knightfall

**Foes:** Dick Grayson, Batman, Batgirl

### POWERS AND ABILITIES

Near superhuman strength, endurance, speed, and durability; almost mindless, with an uncontrollable berserker rage.

### RIOT ON THE STREETS

Confused and easily disorientated, Amygdala was once hired by the villain Knightfall to cause havoc on Gotham City's streets alongside other villains including the Mad Hatter, Clayface, and Mr. Zsasz.

**During the infamous** Gotham City blackout, a mentally unstable behemoth of a man named Aaron Helzinger was undergoing brain surgery. Waking on the operating table—and lacking his brain's rage-controlling amygdala—he smashed his way out of the hospital and began to rampage through the streets. He chanced upon a young Dick Grayson and earned his nickname, Amygdala.

> *"...it hurtsssss!"*

Grayson and his friends and performers at Haly's Circus escaped Amygdala's clutches, subduing the monster when he fell from a rooftop ledge.

# THE RED HOOD GANG

## VITAL STATS

**Team Name:** The Red Hood Gang

**Base:** Gotham City

**Allies:** Fellow Red Hood members

**Foes:** Batman, G.C.P.D., the Penguin, the Falcone Family

**Members:**
Red Hood One (possibly the Joker), the original Red Hood One (Liam Distal), Philip Kane, dozens of mysterious members

### A PLAGUE ON GOTHAM CITY

The citizens of Gotham City lived in fear during the Red Hood Gang's reign of terror. The well-dressed thugs robbed banks, destroyed buildings, and made the city streets unsafe. Most people were too afraid to stand up to the violent gang—but not Bruce Wayne.

**When Bruce Wayne** returned home from training abroad, Gotham City was plagued by the Red Hood Gang. Led by the notorious Red Hood One, the gang was taking over some of the Falcone gang's territory. Before he adopted his identity as Batman, Bruce opposed the gang, only to have them destroy his operations base near Crime Alley, almost killing him in the process.

*"Gotham's Finest!*
*Kill them all!"*

After Bruce was injured by the Red Hood Gang, he realized he had to become more than a man to take them on—and so his Batman persona was born.

# ANARKY

## VITAL STATS

**Real Name:** Sam Young

**Occupation:** Criminal anarchist

**Height:** 6ft 2in

**Weight:** 215 lbs

**Base:** Gotham City

**Allies:** Cult of followers

**Foes:** Batman, the Mad Hatter, Harvey Bullock

## POWERS AND ABILITIES

Natural leader and extremely manipulative; highly intelligent; commands a cult-like army of devoted followers; many connections in the political world.

### FOR THE PEOPLE?

Although he was later proven a fraud by the combined efforts of Batman and Harvey Bullock, Anarky managed to inspire many people during his crusade, including a young man named Lonnie Machin.

**When Anarky emerged** in Gotham City, he brought with him a revolution. However, it was all smoke and mirrors. When Sam Young was a child, his sister was killed by the Mad Hatter. Wanting revenge, Young adopted the identity of Anarky and killed the Hatter's old cohort under cover of the fake rebellion. Batman stopped the villain before he could kill the Hatter.

*"Shape your own future. The Anarky revolution begins today."*

Anarky handed out thousands of masks based on his sister's face, and encouraged Gotham City's citizens to start their lives anew.

# MIRROR

## VITAL STATS

**Real Name:** Jonathan Mills
**Occupation:** Criminal,
former federal agent
**Height:** 6ft
**Weight:** 205 lbs
**Base:** Gotham City
**Allies:** Knightfall,
Grotesque, Gretel
**Foes:** Batgirl,
James Gordon

## POWERS AND ABILITIES

Highly skilled fighter;
extremely athletic; trained
former federal agent;
expert marksman;
protective suit includes
spiked knuckles and Utility
Belt equipped with weapons
and small gadgets.

### TWISTED REFLECTION

Mirror keeps a list
of individuals he believes
should have died, and
does his best to remedy
that "oversight." One such
name was James Gordon,
before Batgirl interfered
and saved her father's life.

**Federal agent Jonathan Mills** was
the only survivor of a car crash that
took the lives of his wife and twin
daughters. He felt he had been fated
to die, and decided to dedicate his life
to killing others whom he believed
should not have survived their near
death experiences. After clashing
with Batgirl, he later went to work
for the criminal Knightfall.

*"And you're not on the list."*

Mirror was one of the first villains Batgirl fought
after returning to life as a vigilante. So naturally,
she was a bit nervous when facing him.

# ARCHITECT

## VITAL STATS

**Real Name:** Dillon May

**Occupation:** Criminal

**Height:** 6ft

**Weight:** 197 lbs

**Base:** Gotham City

**Allies:** Hush, Nicholas and Bradley Gates

**Foes:** Batman, the Batman Family

## POWERS AND ABILITIES

Modified construction suit grants him durability, speed, enhanced strength, and endurance; suit's limited oxygen supply allows for periods of underwater activity; mentally unbalanced with a serious vendetta against Gotham City's most powerful families.

### GATES OF GOTHAM CITY

When Dillon May adopted the suit of the Architect, he had no idea he was basing his vendetta on the words of a madman. Extended suit use leads to severe decompression sickness, and caused Dillon to lose his grip on reality.

Oxygen reserve allows for underwater use

Costume retains its 1800's steampunk style

Hydraulics increase wearer's speed

**In the late 1800s**, Nicholas and Bradley Gates helped construct most of Gotham City's important buildings. Bradley made an underwater suit, but when he was murdered, Nicholas put on the suit to kill the likely culprit. Decades later, Gates's descendant, Dillon May, donned the suit, called himself the Architect, and began destroying Gotham City's historical buildings.

*"...I wonder if you might come out and play?"*

# KILLER MOTH

## VITAL STATS

**Real Name:** Drury Walker
**Occupation:** Criminal
**Height:** 6ft 2in
**Weight:** 210 lbs
**Base:** Mobile
**Allies:** Richard Dragon II, Red Dart, Brick, Count Vertigo
**Foes:** Batman, Green Arrow

## POWERS AND ABILITIES

Uses hi-tech compression gun called a "stinger" to deliver highly concentrated air blasts; has many connections in the criminal underworld.

## LIKE A MOTH TO A FLAME

Never one to pass up an opportunity, Killer Moth decided to work for a criminal calling himself Richard Dragon in Seattle. His mission was to take over the city and kill the hero Green Arrow in the process.

Compression gun hooked to tanks

Wears gas mask to hide his identity

Calls his gun his "stinger"

**Years ago, during** a terrifying superstorm that hit Gotham City, a woman called Moira Queen lent a hand during the crisis. Killer Moth, who was just starting his criminal career, decided to kidnap the wealthy woman. Unfortunately for the trigger-happy Killer Moth, Batman arrived to stop him, along with Moira's son, the fledgling Super Hero, Green Arrow.

*"You're in Gotham now... everyone's a freak!"*

# BONE

## VITAL STATS

**Real Name:** Louis Ferryman

**Occupation:** Criminal

**Height:** 6ft 2in

**Weight:** 215 lbs

**Base:** Gotham City

**Allies:** Tiger Shark, Dragos Ibanescu

**Foes:** Catwoman, Batman, Killer Croc

## POWERS AND ABILITIES

Organized mid-level crime boss with connections in Gotham City's criminal underworld; holds grudges easily; often uses firearms; quite wealthy; employs criminals who wear white skull masks.

### A BONE TO PICK

Catwoman first ran afoul of Bone when she stole from him. Enraged by her actions, he had his men destroy her apartment and kill her business partner, Lola MacIntire. He has maintained a grudge against Catwoman ever since.

**Louis Ferryman** came from a poor family in Gotham City. He often moved, living at his parents' place, then his aunt's, then a group home. Bothered that fellow housemates would steal his things, Louis climbed the ranks of the criminal scene, taking pride in finally owning belongings. He adopted the name Bone and found true pleasure in owning jewelry, art, and rare coins.

*"Welcome, one 'n' all, to the great cat massacre."*

Wears white suit and matching tie

Skin has texture and color of human bone

Hires thugs to do his dirty work

# DR. PHOSPHORUS

## VITAL STATS

**Real Name:** Alexander Sartorius

**Occupation:** Criminal, underground tribe leader

**Height:** 5ft 11in

**Weight:** 169 lbs

**Base:** Gotham City

**Allies:** Deacon Blackfire, Tinderbox

**Foes:** Batman, Catwoman, the Joker's Daughter

## POWERS AND ABILITIES

Can shoot radioactive phosphorus flame at enemies; burns constantly with poisonous fumes; brilliant mind and natural leader; commands army of underground citizens.

### RING OF FIRE

When clashing with Catwoman and the Joker's Daughter in the Gotham City underground, Dr. Phosphorus revealed that his ultimate desire was to turn Gotham City into a giant volcano by causing explosions in the underground.

**Catwoman first stumbled across** Dr. Phosphorus when she was searching for her friend Rat-Tail in the vast passageways under Gotham City. She passed into Charneltown, the area that Phosphorus ruled with his daughter, Tinderbox. Phosphorus revealed that he had been the victim of a nuclear accident and had fled to Charneltown so he could live somewhere hot.

*"...I could flick my finger and fry you to a cinder."*

When Dr. Phosphorus was imprisoned in Arkham Asylum, doctors summoned some of the country's top scientists to work out how to stop him from burning.

# THE CREEPER

## VITAL STATS

**Real Name:** Jack Ryder

**Occupation:** Criminal, former reporter

**Height:** 6ft

**Weight:** 194 lbs

**Base:** Mobile

**Ally:** Killer Croc

**Foes:** Katana, Batman

## POWERS AND ABILITIES

Hosts a mystical demon; superhuman strength, agility, endurance, and durability; able to leap far distances; carries chains that he uses as weapons; can create manufactured tornadoes with his chains.

### CREEPING THROUGH

The Oni Demon known as the Creeper came to our reality through a "crack in the world" during 16th century Japan. Twenty years later, he was discovered and imprisoned in the magical Soultaker sword.

**Jack Ryder, a famous** TV personality, was killed while reporting on a giant monster. Meanwhile, the Super Hero Katana was locked in battle with Killer Croc, who shattered her Soultaker sword, freeing a demon called the Creeper. These seemingly unrelated events converged when the Creeper took possession of Ryder's body, resurrecting Jack in the process.

*"The Creeper rides again."*

When Katana pieced her Soultaker sword back together, the Creeper became one of the main targets on her list.

# DEACON BLACKFIRE

ROGUE

## VITAL STATS

**Full Name:** Joseph Blackfire
**Occupation:** Criminal, cultist
**Height:** 6ft 3in
**Weight:** 228 lbs
**Base:** Gotham City
**Allies:** Professor Milo,
Mr. Bygone, the Joker's
Daughter, Maxie Zeus,
Dr. Phosphorus
**Foes:** Batman, Batwing,
Jim Corrigan

## POWERS AND ABILITIES

Confident leader with
natural charisma; uses
violent techniques to gain
followers; commands an
army of devoted cultists.

### BLACKFIRE AND BRIMSTONE

As an influential speaker,
Blackfire gained a loyal army by
finding people who had slipped
through society's cracks. He lured
them to his ranks by promising
them all salvation under his rule.

**Deacon Joseph Blackfire** used to give
sermons about the evils of Gotham
City. Though he preached love, he
was more interested in gaining power
as the leader of his cult. He kidnapped
Batman and used sleep deprivation
and other violent methods to wear
him down, but the Dark Knight
escaped. Batman proved to everyone
that the villain Blackfire was a fraud.

*"My holy flock, our
time grows near!"*

Deacon Blackfire returned from the dead to plague
Gotham City. He commanded an army of undead
spirits, but was ultimately defeated by the Spectre.

# FRIGHT

## VITAL STATS

**Real Name:** Linda Friitawa

**Occupation:** Criminal, former geneticist

**Height:** 5ft 9in

**Weight:** 143 lbs

**Base:** Gotham City

**Allies:** Scarecrow, the Penguin

**Foes:** Batman, the Batman Family, Batwoman

### POWERS AND ABILITIES

Can exhale nerve toxins; superhuman agility and strength; advanced medical knowledge; expert in genetics; adept hand-to-hand combatant.

### FRIGHT NIGHT

Fright escaped Arkham Asylum during a mass breakout, but was soon imprisoned again. She was a useful source of information for Batwoman when the Super Hero was researching Batman and his methods.

**A disgraced geneticist** who lost her medical license, Linda Friitawa began secretly experimenting on her boss, Dr. Jonathan Crane—also known as Scarecrow. After transforming him into a Scarebeast, Friitawa adopted the name Fright and became a super-villain, spending her criminal career in and out of Arkham Asylum, taking advantage of the frequent breakouts.

*"I can kill him with one breath, love!"*

Linda Friitawa can exhale nerve toxins. In order to keep her powers in check, the guards at Arkham Asylum have to keep a breathing mask on her.

# ANCHORESS

## VITAL STATS

**Real Name:** Unknown

**Occupation:** Arkham Asylum inmate

**Height:** 5ft 2in

**Weight:** 84 lbs

**Base:** Gotham City

**Allies:** Dr. Jeremiah Arkham, Dr. Amadeus Arkham

**Foes:** Batman, the Joker's Daughter

## POWERS AND ABILITIES

Has the ability to "quantum tunnel," or walk through walls; able to toy with the minds and memories of her victims; able to alter her own appearance.

## BLAMING THE BAT

The Anchoress wrongly blames Batman for turning Arkham Asylum into a terrible place, rather than the peaceful asylum it used to be before the emergence of villains like the Joker and Mr. Zsasz.

**Born sometime before** the 1900s, the woman who would become the Anchoress was interested in physics. When her parents tried to marry her off, a struggle ensued, ending with the Anchoress being knocked into a shelf full of chemicals. The resulting explosion killed her parents and gave her new abilities that enabled her to project her body's energy through various objects.

*"They've all forgotten me here..."*

Appears helpless and frail

Can alter her appearance

Can enter one's mind with a touch

# REAPER

**ROGUE**

## VITAL STATS

**Real Name:** Dr. Benjamin Gruener

**Occupation:** Criminal

**Height:** 5ft 10in

**Weight:** 166 lbs

**Base:** Gotham City

**Allies:** Bane, Blackgate Penitentiary Inmates

**Foes:** Batman, the Falcone Family, Sumo, Firefly

## POWERS AND ABILITIES

Wears armored suit that strikes fear into those who encounter it; well-versed in medicine; adept hand-to-hand fighter; gauntlets contain sickle blades and firearms.

### FLOWERS AT THE GRAVE

Batman recently battled the Reaper in the back of a floral truck with the help of Robin. The Reaper was attempting to send poisonous flowers to a wake for a member of the Falcone family.

**Benjamin Gruener grew** up in Germany during World War II, and was a survivor of the holocaust. He became a medical doctor, but his past made him fixate on revenge and he lost his sanity. As the Reaper, he has mysteriously cheated death to seek deadly justice for Gotham City's criminals, although he often clashes with the metropolis's true champion, the Batman.

*"Now it's time to die."*

After a riot in Blackgate Penitentiary instigated by Bane's forces, the Reaper joined Bane in a fight against the Arkham Asylum inmates.

## VITAL STATS

**Real Name:** Guillermo Barrera

**Occupation:** Criminal, enforcer

**Height:** 5ft 4in

**Weight:** 145 lbs

**Base:** Mobile

**Allies:** La Dama, Coyote, Rompe-Huesos

**Foes:** Dick Grayson, Blue Beetle, Brotherhood of Evil

### POWERS AND ABILITIES

Expert with blade weapons, especially throwing knives; capable hand-to-hand combatant; extremely athletic and agile.

### UNLUCKY SHOT

While quite formidable with his throwing knives, Brutale was actually instrumental in the creation of the Super Hero Blue Beetle. When one of his knives pierced the alien scarab Jaime Reyes was carrying at the time, the device was activated and turned Jaime into the Blue Beetle.

**Hailing from Hasaragua,** Guillermo Barrera was a deadly interrogator for his government's secret police, with a fondness for bladed weapons. When the regime changed, he set out into the world of freelance crime, as Brutale. After fighting Nightwing, Brutale worked for crime boss La Dama in El Paso, Texas, where he fought Blue Beetle and lost.

*"—the little hero won't get far with a blade in his spine."*

Brutale's costume is covered with throwing knives. While they might appear ornamental, Brutale can and will use every blade at his disposal.

ROGUE

## VITAL STATS

**Real Name:** Dr. Thomas Wayne

**Occupation:** Criminal

**Height:** 6ft

**Weight:** 205 lbs

**Base:** Gotham City

**Allies:** The Club of Villains, the Black Glove

**Foes:** Batman, Robin

## POWERS AND ABILITIES

Master manipulator and plotter; does not age; extremely smart; very wealthy, with connections in high society, the worldwide underworld, the supernatural world, and various secret societies; capable hand-to-hand combatant.

## ALLEGED ALLEGIANCE

Dr. Hurt wanted to defeat Batman, and saw Robin as a useful pawn in his game. He offered to spare Robin's life if he swore to be his partner. But Robin already had a teammate, and he and Batman soon showed the doctor the true meaning of "Hurt."

**While he is indeed** Dr. Thomas Wayne, Dr. Hurt is not Bruce Wayne's father, but an ancestor who cheated death by releasing a devil called Barbatos back in 1765. Centuries later, Hurt met Batman and planted seeds of defeat in his mind by posing as a psychologist early in the Dark Knight's career. Hurt later triggered Batman's mental breakdown in an attempt to kill the hero.

*"...the Dark Knight is dead. Here's to crime. And the Black Glove."*

With his own fail-safe programming buried deep in his mind, Batman was able to overcome Dr. Hurt's mental manipulation.

# THE CLUB OF VILLAINS

## VITAL STATS

**Team Name:** The Club of Villains

**Base:** Gotham City

**Allies:** The Black Glove

**Foes:** Batman, the Batman Family, the Club of Heroes

**Members:** Dr. Simon Hurt, Charlie Caligula, Scorpiana, El Sombrero, Le Bossu, Swagman, King Kraken, Pierrot Lunaire

### THE CLUB SCENE
When Dr. Hurt attacked Batman directly, the rest of the Club of Villains attacked Batman's allies. However, the Club of Heroes arrived in Gotham City to even the odds and give Batman time to triumph over the Black Glove.

**Dr. Hurt waited decades** to take over Gotham City, and had meanwhile formed many alliances with nefarious groups, including the Club of Villains. Created as the counterpart to Batman's allies in the Club of Heroes, the villains hailed from all over the globe. Many of them had clashed with Club of Heroes members, such as El Gaucho. The Club was a small part of Hurt's larger conspiracy, the Black Glove.

*"Come, take your place for the danse macabre."*

Batman gained a whole new Rogues Gallery when Dr. Hurt assembled his Club of Villains, and many of the villains have gone on to challenge Batman, Inc.

# DR. DEATH

ROGUE

## VITAL STATS

**Real Name:** Dr. Karl Helfern
**Occupation:** Former scientist
**Height:** Varies with mutations
**Weight:** Varies with mutations
**Base:** Gotham City
**Allies:** The Riddler, Crazy Quilt, Dr. Hugo Strange
**Foes:** Batman, Poison Ivy, James Gordon, Lucius Fox

## POWERS AND ABILITIES

Superhuman strength, endurance, and durability; armed with serum that causes rapid bone growth to the point of death; brilliant scientist; body constantly healing in strange new bone formations.

## DEATH COMES KNOCKING

After becoming unstable and losing his job at Wayne Enterprises, Dr. Death injected himself with an experimental bone-hardening formula, adopting a monstrous form. He used his new abilities to kill his former colleagues, under the Riddler's employ.

**Years ago, during** a citywide blackout, the police discovered a series of grotesque murder victims. The culprit was Dr. Death, a mysterious man who earned his nickname by experimenting on animals in illegal labs. After looking into Dr. Death's past, Batman battled the villain above Gotham City, a fight that Death seemingly didn't survive.

> *"I've been waiting so long to meet you, after all."*

Brilliant mind bent on revenge

Serum causes elongated proportions

Teeth grown into disturbing fangs

# JACKANAPES

## VITAL STATS

**Real Name:** Jackanapes
**Occupation:** Criminal
**Height:** 7ft 3in
**Weight:** 453 lbs
**Base:** Gotham City
**Ally:** The Joker
**Foes:** Batman, the
Batman Family

## POWERS AND ABILITIES

Typical strength, stamina,
and endurance of a large
gorilla; quick learner.

### FUTURE THREAT

According to the Joker, Jackanapes was
a fast learner and could even work on
intricate machinery. If true, this intelligent
gorilla could prove to be a major foe of
Batman in the future.

**One day, at Gotham** County Zoo,
the Joker spotted a baby gorilla
playing with a stuffed monkey toy,
similar to one he had as a child.
The Joker kidnapped the gorilla and
began to raise it as his own, training
it in the ways of murder. However,
Jackanapes seemingly died when he
was knocked off a blimp during one
of the Joker's elaborate crimes.

"..."

Trained in
operating
firearms

Jester costume
complements
the Joker's

Armed with
deadly weapons
at all times

# JAMES GORDON, JR.

**ROGUE**

## VITAL STATS

**Full Name:** James Gordon, Jr.

**Occupation:** Criminal

**Height:** 5ft 10in

**Weight:** 159 lbs

**Base:** Gotham City

**Allies:** Knightfall, Suicide Squad

**Foes:** Batgirl, James Gordon, Barbara Kean Gordon

## POWERS AND ABILITIES

Psychotic master plotter and manipulator; many underworld connections; extremely intelligent; expert at covering up his crimes; aware of Batgirl's double life.

### KILLER INSTINCT

When James Gordon, Jr. reemerged in Batgirl's life, he played twisted games with his sister, even attempting to kill their mother, Barbara Kean Gordon. During one dramatic fight, Batgirl defeated James, mistakenly believing she'd killed him.

As a baby, **James Gordon, Jr.** never cried, and as he got older, his family could sense coldness behind his eyes. When James killed the family cat and threatened the same violence to his sister Barbara, his mother left, abandoning Barbara in the process. Barbara grew up to become Batgirl, while James grew up to be every bit as evil as his family knew him to be.

> *"You. Will. Never. Be free of me."*

James knows Barbara Gordon well enough to manipulate her. He even let Batgirl believe he was dead while he served as a Suicide Squad advisor.

# BLACK MASK

## VITAL STATS

**Real Name:** Roman Sionis
**Occupation:** Criminal
**Height:** 6ft 1in
**Weight:** 195 lbs
**Base:** Gotham City
**Allies:** The False Face Society
**Foes:** Batman, the Mad Hatter

### POWERS AND ABILITIES

Wears ebony mask that seems to give him telepathic and telekinetic powers; natural leader; expert strategist; capable hand-to-hand combatant; very intelligent; expert in torture techniques.

### MASK VS. HAT

Black Mask's father's casket has long been one of the holy grails for the Mad Hatter, another of Batman's foes obsessed with mind control. This put the Hatter and Black Mask at odds, and made them natural rivals.

**The rich yet disturbed heir** to the Janus Cosmetics company, Roman Sionis was rumored to have played an active part in his parents' death when their home burned to the ground. Obsessed with masks, Roman carved his infamous black mask out of his father's coffin, later discovering that the casket was made of a strange material that gave him special abilities.

*"Can't you see your mind is too weak to defend against my probe?!"*

Uses mask to control False Face Society

Accustomed to wearing expensive clothes

Fancy suit juxtaposed with frightful mask terrifies foes

# BLACK SPIDER

## VITAL STATS

**Real Name:** Eric Needham
**Occupation:** Vigilante
**Height:** 5ft 10in
**Weight:** 173 lbs
**Base:** Gotham City
**Ally:** Basilisk
**Foes:** Batman, Suicide
Squad, Amanda Waller

### POWERS AND ABILITIES

Master martial artist;
wears armored suit
equipped with a variety
of weapons and devices;
weapons expert who
often uses kamas;
excellent athlete and
gymnast; strong desire
to seek vengeance
against all criminals.

## EYE OF THE SPIDER

Black Spider's mask is equipped with special
lenses that allow him to utilize thermal imaging
and get a better read on his target, even in a
room that's pitch black or obscured by smoke.

**When government agent** Amanda
Waller proposed the idea of the
Suicide Squad, a task force of
super-villains that offered her
complete deniability, Black Spider
was a top choice on her list of
recruits. An old enemy of Batman,
Black Spider was a Gotham City
vigilante whose violent methods proved
too extreme for the Dark Knight.

*"I'm not done here yet."*

While on the Suicide Squad, Black Spider proved
he was as corrupt as ever when he betrayed the
team to the terrorist organization called Basilisk.

# MAXIE ZEUS

ROGUE

## VITAL STATS

**Full Name:** Maximilian Zeus

**Occupation:** Criminal

**Height:** 5ft 6in

**Weight:** 135 lbs

**Base:** Gotham City

**Allies:** Deacon Blackfire, Professor Milo, the Joker's Daughter

**Foes:** Batman, Batwing, the Batman Family

## POWERS AND ABILITIES

Fit and athletic; capable hand-to-hand combatant; intelligent natural leader with a severe god complex; many connections in the business world and the criminal underworld.

### THE POWER OF ZEUS

While staying in Arkham Asylum, Maxie Zeus was rendered near catatonic and felt nothing. This made him especially difficult to best in a fight, as the hero Batwing soon discovered firsthand.

For a time, **Maxie Zeus** was a successful crime boss in Gotham City. However, he began to lose his grip on reality and think of himself as a god, despite being bested by his enemy, the Batman. Later sentenced to a stay in Arkham Asylum, Zeus briefly hosted the spirit of Deacon Blackfire in his own body. This led to a battle with Batwing and the Spectre.

> **"Bow down *to me*, mortal."**

Zeus was treated like the god he believed he was when he joined a cult intent on resurrecting Deacon Blackfire, whose spirit possessed his body.

# EMPEROR BLACKGATE

ROGUE

## VITAL STATS

**Real Name:** Ignatius Ogilvy
**Occupation:** Criminal
**Height:** 6ft 3in
**Weight:** 225 lbs
**Base:** Gotham City
**Allies:** Poison Ivy,
Mr. Mosaic, Hypnotic,
Imperceptible Man,
Mr. Zsasz
**Foes:** Batman, the Penguin,
the Batman Family

## POWERS AND ABILITIES

Brilliant strategist who
quickly climbed the criminal
ranks; superhuman
strength and durability
from serum partially
created by Poison Ivy.

## KING OF THE MOUNTAIN

After powering himself
up with a combination
of Man-Bat serum,
Venom, and a plant-
based formula,
Emperor Penguin was
arrested and taken to
jail. There he quickly
became the so-called
king of the prison,
changing his moniker
to Emperor Blackgate.

**Ignatius Ogilvy rose** to power as the
Penguin's right hand man. But when
the Joker forced the Penguin to help
him in his latest scheme, Ogilvy
claimed the Penguin's empire for
his own as Emperor Penguin. He
injected himself with a secret formula
to become a physical threat, but was
ultimately defeated by Batman and
incarcerated in Blackgate Penitentiary.

Unafraid to steal
the Penguin's
fashion and title

Master
manipulator
with high IQ

Powerful
connections in
the underworld

> *"The dawn of a new era...and the
> empire of Emperor Penguin."*

# FIREBUG

ROGUE

## VITAL STATS

**Real Name:** Unknown

**Occupation:** Criminal, arsonist

**Height:** 5ft 9in

**Weight:** 180 lbs

**Base:** Gotham City

**Allies:** Various employers

**Foes:** Batgirl, Batman

## POWERS AND ABILITIES

Uses military grade fast-burning accelerant to start and spread fires; wears protective fireproof armor; employs rocket launchers and incendiary grenades; single-minded focus on his mission once hired.

### SOLDIER OF FORTUNE?

Little is known about Firebug's past, but the medals he wears on his otherwise unadorned suit imply a military background. He is obviously highly skilled, and shows no signs of guilt or remorse for his actions.

**While probably not** as well known as the similar Gotham City villain, Firefly, Firebug doesn't let the competition get to him. As a freelance arsonist, Firebug takes his jobs seriously, recently clashing with Batgirl when she was tracking down accomplices of the Joker. Killing police officers at the behest of his employer, Firebug was eventually defeated by the determined Batgirl.

*"You shouldn't have come here to mess with Firebug, girl!"*

Firebug's suit seems more utilitarian than those of most costumed criminals. A consummate professional, he prides himself on his work.

# FIREFLY

## VITAL STATS

**Real Name:** Ted Carson

**Occupation:** Criminal

**Height:** 5ft 11in

**Weight:** 167 lbs

**Base:** Gotham City

**Allies:** Cluemaster, Lock-Up, Signalman

**Foes:** Batman, Dick Grayson, Batgirl, the Batman Family

### POWERS AND ABILITIES

Uses stolen Firefly suit that is capable of flight and protects wearer from heat and other damage; suit can fire blasts of flame; equipped with flame sword and incendiary grenades.

### FLY VS. FLY

Ted Carson stole technology and the name Firefly from Garfield Lynns, a talented, yet easily angered pyrotechnics expert. His advanced Firefly suit can fly with the use of fiery wings.

**Movie star Cindy Cooke** had lots of adoring and obsessive fans. So when her talent agency, production company, and the home of her ex-boyfriend, Ted Carson, burned down, there were plenty of suspects. It took the combined efforts of Nightwing and Batgirl to discover that Carson himself was the Firefly, having faked his own death in order to live a private life with Cindy.

*"I'm sorry...but this is personal."*

As Firefly, Carson attempted to frame the deceased Garfield Lynns for his crimes, but all his attacks were merely an elaborate smokescreen.

# GENTLEMAN GHOST

## VITAL STATS

**Real Name:** Jim Craddock
**Occupation:** Criminal
**Height:** 5ft 11in
**Weight:** 174 lbs
**Base:** Gotham City
**Allies:** The undead
**Foes:** Batman, Batwing, Midnight Shift, Hawkman

## POWERS AND ABILITIES

Ghost-like, with the ability to phase through objects at will; naturally charming; highly intelligent; a master plotter; can project bug-like appendages from his body to aid in fighting; able to alter his flesh to appear invisible or like that of a horrible monster; can be driven away by Nth metal.

### TO THE NTH DEGREE

Despite his sometimes monstrous appearance, the Gentleman Ghost can often charm those that cross his path. One surefire way to keep him at bay, however, is by using the Thanagarian element, Nth metal.

**Although his story remains** unconfirmed, due to his tendency to fabricate a tale or two, the super-villain calling himself the Gentleman Ghost claims to not be a ghost at all. Hundreds of years ago, Jim Craddock was cursed by a witch who made him do her thievery. After her death, the Gentleman Ghost continued his criminal career, clashing with Hawkman and later, Batman.

*"Take it from me...dead lasts a very long time!"*

Hawkman first crossed paths with the Gentleman Ghost when the Ghost was searching for an artifact that could vanquish armies of the dead.

# FLAMINGO

## VITAL STATS

**Full Name:** Eduardo Flamingo

**Occupation:** Enforcer, assassin

**Height:** 6ft 3in

**Weight:** 199 lbs

**Base:** Gotham City

**Allies:** Hush, Penitente Cartel

**Foes:** Batman, Red Hood, the Batman Family

### POWERS AND ABILITIES

Expert hand-to-hand combatant; weapons expert, particularly skilled in use of whips, swords, and firearms; feared throughout the criminal underworld; expert motorcycle driver; lobotomized and unpredictable.

### PRETTY HORRIFIC IN PINK

The Flamingo's colorful uniform and flair for pizazz hide the truly lethal skills of this masked murderer. He more often than not can be found atop his pink motorcycle, using his whip with deadly results.

**The killer named Flamingo** had created quite a reputation for himself before he arrived in Gotham City to challenge Batman and Robin. As an alpha-enforcer for the greedy Penitente Cartel, he was known for showing no mercy. Attracted to Gotham City by the actions of the Red Hood, Flamingo fought Dick Grayson, who only defeated him with the Red Hood's help.

*"Heh Heh Heh."*

The Flamingo once challenged Batman in his Batmobile, but the Batmobile trumps a motorcycle in any fight. Batman easily took the villain down.

# LARK

## VITAL STATS

**Real Name:** Unknown
**Occupation:** Criminal
**Height:** 5ft 7in
**Weight:** 132 lbs
**Base:** Gotham City
**Ally:** The Penguin
**Foes:** Batman, the Batman Family

### POWERS AND ABILITIES

Excellent hand-to-hand combatant; adept with firearms; cool under pressure; access to the Penguin's impressive information network.

### BIRDS OF A FEATHER

Aside from serving as the Penguin's chauffeur and bodyguard, Lark is also the villain's sounding board. She is privy to information others in his organization are not, and is often an accomplice to his horrendous crimes.

**As a general rule,** the Penguin likes to surround himself with beautiful women to serve as bodyguards. While some of his employees, like Black Canary and Starling, didn't quite work out, others have stayed by his side through thick and thin, such as Lark. She is often tasked with keeping a watchful eye over the Penguin while aboard his floating Iceberg Casino.

*"Your wish is our command, Mr. Penguin."*

Wears earpiece to keep informed

Always ready for a fight

Normally dressed all in black

Carries handgun on person at all times

# GREAT WHITE SHARK

## VITAL STATS

**Real Name:** Warren White
**Occupation:** Criminal
**Height:** 5ft 11in
**Weight:** 185 lbs
**Base:** Gotham City
**Allies:** Humpty Dumpty, Tally Man
**Foes:** Batman, the Batman Family

## POWERS AND ABILITIES

Adept hand-to-hand combatant; keeps himself in top physical condition; has teeth filed to sharp points; brilliant strategist and schemer; has no moral compass.

### SHARK ATTACK
Despite being held at Arkham Asylum, the Great White Shark has managed to run a powerful criminal empire from behind bars. He is a far cry from the "new fish" who was terrified to even enter the asylum a while ago.

**Called "the Great White Shark"** by the press, Warren White perpetrated one of the greatest acts of financial fraud in history. But instead of doing hard time, White pled insanity.
The judge was not deceived and sent him to Arkham Asylum where White truly began to resemble his nickname when he lost his nose and ears while trapped in Mr. Freeze's refrigerated cell.

### *"Who's the new fish?"*

Great White Shark wasted no time in leaping into the fray during a recent battle between Arkham's inmates and those of Blackgate Penitentiary.

# PROFESSOR MILO

## VITAL STATS

**Real Name:** Achilles Milo

**Occupation:** Criminal, former professor at Gotham Academy

**Height:** 6ft

**Weight:** 160 lbs

**Base:** Gotham City

**Allies:** Deacon Blackfire, the Joker's Daughter, Maxie Zeus

**Foes:** Batman, the Batman Family

## POWERS AND ABILITIES

Expert in chemistry with a genius-level IQ; expert plotter and manipulator; many connections in the criminal underworld.

### RUNNING MAN

After his latest scheme at Arkham was foiled by the intervention of the supernatural hero called the Spectre, Professor Milo tried to flee the country but was stopped by the Batman and his newest Batplane.

**Often using his expertise** to obtain positions of authority, Professor Milo is a talented chemist who has put his knowledge to evil ends many times. Most recently, Milo posed as a doctor at Arkham Asylum, sneaking patients into underground chambers for cult leader Deacon Blackfire. He was also a teacher at Gotham Academy until his corruption became apparent.

*"...this man is suffering. He wants us to help him."*

When allied with the cultist Deacon Blackfire, Milo used his knowledge of chemistry to drug Blackfire's recruits, forcing them to obey him.

# HUMPTY DUMPTY

## VITAL STATS

**Real Name:** Humphry Dumpler

**Occupation:** Criminal

**Height:** 6ft 3in

**Weight:** 349 lbs

**Base:** Gotham City

**Ally:** Great White Shark

**Foes:** Batman, Batgirl, the Batman Family

## POWERS AND ABILITIES

Disturbed mind with a penchant for breaking things and trying to put them back together again; appears to have the intellect of a child; has a large body with substantial strength.

## ALL FALL DOWN

Humpty Dumpty almost single-handedly changed the face of Gotham City by inadvertently destroying many of the large over-the-top props that formerly graced the town's famous skyline.

**Humphry Dumpler's life** fell apart after his home was destroyed by a misplaced wrecking ball. He soon became obsessed with taking things apart and putting them back again, including subway cars and traffic lights. Dubbed Humpty Dumpty, the unbalanced Dumpler caused an untold number of injuries due to the fact that he couldn't quite repair the damage he created.

> *"Snips and snails and puppy dog tails."*

Often a resident at Arkham Asylum, Humpty Dumpty is not very popular—since he sometimes likes to "fix" people he views as broken.

# HYPNOTIC

## VITAL STATS

**Real Name:** Unknown
**Occupation:** Criminal
**Height:** 6ft
**Weight:** 197 lbs
**Base:** Gotham City
**Allies:** The Penguin, Mr. Combustible, Mr. Toxic, Imperceptible Man, Mr. Mosaic, Emperor Blackgate
**Foes:** Batman, the Batman Family, the Falcone Family

## POWERS AND ABILITIES

Highly intelligent; utilizes radio control waves to take over the minds of his victims; maintains powerful connections in the criminal underworld.

### THE EYES HAVE IT

Hypnotic saw himself facing action in Gotham City sooner than expected when he battled Batman while aboard the Penguin's Iceberg Casino. He quickly discovered his hypnotic abilities had no effect on the Dark Knight.

**Hypnotic made his debut** in Gotham City along with several other new players who were organized and mentored by the Penguin. As part of his mentorship, Hypnotic was forced to pay part of his earnings to the Penguin. So when the Penguin's empire was briefly taken over by Emperor Blackgate, Hypnotic had no qualms about switching allegiances.

Highly intelligent crime boss

Uses radio waves to control minds

Shows little loyalty to anyone

*"Stand back. I'll take control—"*

# IMPERCEPTIBLE MAN

## VITAL STATS

**Real Name:** Unknown
**Occupation:** Criminal
**Height:** Unknown
**Weight:** Unknown
**Base:** Gotham City
**Allies:** The Penguin, Mr. Toxic, Mr. Combustible, Hypnotic, Mr. Mosaic, Emperor Blackgate
**Foes:** Batman, the Batman Family, the Falcone Family

### POWERS AND ABILITIES

Is completely invisible except for the clothing he chooses to wear; highly intelligent; many useful connections in the criminal underworld.

### MARCHING ORDERS

Having previously worked for the Penguin, the Imperceptible Man and a few of his fellow criminals were called to a meeting by their temporary boss Ignatius Ogilvy, the future Emperor Blackgate.

Always wears glasses

Natural leader and crime boss, despite being invisible

Clothes do not turn invisible like his skin

Wore gas mask during the Man-Bat epidemic

**The Imperceptible Man** is a mysterious criminal whose powers remain a mystery to the majority of Gotham City's citizens. An employee of the Penguin, the Imperceptible Man's work was interrupted by a brief stint of cooperation with the Penguin's replacement, Emperor Blackgate, before he and his allies returned to work for the Penguin.

*"What are we going to do?"*

# BIG TOP

## VITAL STATS

**Real Name:** Unknown
**Occupation:** Criminal
**Height:** 5ft 9in
**Weight:** 567 lbs
**Base:** Gotham City
**Allies:** Professor Pyg, Mr. Toad, Le Cirque d'etrange
**Foes:** Dick Grayson, Robin, Batman

## POWERS AND ABILITIES

Excess weight allows for nearly superhuman strength and endurance; excellent hand-to-hand combatant despite size; many connections in the criminal underworld.

### THE BIG MYSTERY

So little is known about Big Top that there is some debate over whether the villain is male or female. Big Top insists upon wearing a tutu nearly all of the time, but has a fully-formed goatee.

**Little is known about** the super-villain Big Top. As a member of Le Cirque d'etrange, Big Top worked directly with Professor Pyg, and even stormed police headquarters to help fellow circus member, Mr. Toad, escape custody. Unfortunately for Big Top, Batman and Robin were on hand to bring the criminals to justice.

*"Didn't Toad tell you he had friends?"*

Weight lends to powerful strikes

Strange appearance intimidates foes

Is quicker than appears

# LOCK-UP

## VITAL STATS

**Real Name:** Lyle Bolton
**Occupation:** Criminal
**Height:** 6ft 2in
**Weight:** 240 lbs
**Base:** Gotham City
**Allies:** Cluemaster, Firefly, Signalman
**Foes:** Batman, the Batman Family, Spoiler

### POWERS AND ABILITIES

Expert knowledge of police procedure; extremely fit and athletic; adept hand-to-hand combatant; known to use police weapons including baton; employs hi-tech weapons as well, including an electrified net.

### IF YOU CAN'T BEAT 'EM...

In a renewed effort to eliminate the threat of Batman for good, Lock-Up teamed with several minor super-villains under the leadership of Cluemaster. Lock-Up and his allies were hoping that their meetings would remain under the radar due to their D-list status.

**Lock-Up is really Lyle Bolton**, a former security guard with a thirst for his own brand of justice. Having tried and failed to become a police officer, Lock-Up has no regard for the legal system. He began kidnapping super-villains and locking them up in makeshift prisons. After the Dark Knight stopped Lock-Up's crusade, Bolton became just another villain in Batman's Rogues Gallery.

*"It's true what they say... it's brutal at the top."*

Maintains private vendetta against injustice

Wears attire similar to police riot gear

Extremely athletic and muscular

# KNIGHTFALL

## VITAL STATS

**Real Name:** Charise Carnes

**Occupation:** Philanthropist, criminal

**Height:** 5ft 11in

**Weight:** 141 lbs

**Base:** Gotham City

**Allies:** Mirror, Grotesque, Gretel, James Gordon, Jr.

**Foes:** Batgirl, the Birds of Prey, Batwoman

## POWERS AND ABILITIES

Expert manipulator and actor; extremely wealthy; adept martial artist with expertise in bladed weapons; severely mentally unhinged; many connections in high society and in the criminal underworld.

### KNIGHTFALL DESCENDING

While the public saw Charise Carnes as a philanthropist trying to help the neighborhood of Cherry Hill, Batgirl discovered her cruelty early on. As Knightfall, Charise wanted to harm or kill every criminal in the city, no matter how minor his crime.

**Raised by a wealthy** real-estate baron, Charise Carnes was a teenager with a boyfriend named Trevor. But Charise was horrified when Trevor killed her family in front of her eyes. She didn't report her boyfriend, however, and was found guilty for his heinous acts. After a stint in Arkham Asylum, she reemerged as Knightfall, kidnapped Trevor, and made him pay for his crime.

> **"We're going to change Gotham forever."**

The villain made a later bid for Gotham City, with many of Batgirl's old enemies. But with help from other female heroes, Batgirl's side prevailed.

# GROTESQUE

## VITAL STATS

**Real Name:** Phillipe Rianne
**Occupation:** Criminal
**Height:** 5ft 11in
**Weight:** 173 lbs
**Base:** Gotham City
**Allies:** Knightfall,
Gretel, Mirror
**Foes:** The Birds of Prey,
Batgirl

## POWERS AND ABILITIES

Superhuman strength
and endurance; mutation
allows for the ability to
absorb and release
electricity.

## LIGHTNING STRIKES

When he first battled
Batgirl, Grotesque surprised
her by absorbing and
redirecting the electricity of
a nearby lamp. When they
battled for a second time,
he threatened to use the
electricity of a storm cloud,
but was shot by a henchman
with a change of heart.

**Batgirl encountered** the mysterious
super-villain called Grotesque when
he crashed a party for media mogul
Theodore Aiklin, demanding that Aiklin
hand over a valuable bottle of wine.
Aiklin refused, Grotesque escaped,
and Batgirl pursued him through the
sewers. He later ambushed her, but
was betrayed by one of his lackeys,
and Batgirl took the villain down.

*"What a lovely vintage she is."*

Wears
gargoyle-like
mask

Mask once
shattered
by Batgirl

Channels
electricity
through club

Considers himself a
cultured individual

Dresses in
expensive
clothing

# GRETEL

## VITAL STATS

**Real Name:** Lisly Bonner

**Occupation:** Criminal

**Height:** 5ft 10in

**Weight:** 140 lbs

**Base:** Gotham City

**Allies:** Knightfall, Grotesque, Mirror

**Foes:** Batgirl, Batman, the Birds of Prey

## POWERS AND ABILITIES

Expert hand-to-hand combatant; inability to feel pain; able to control the minds of men and make them do her bidding; proficient with firearms and knives.

## WORKING FOR CRUMBS

After failing to fulfill a contract to murder Bruce Wayne due to the intervention of Batgirl and Batman, Gretel later continued her life of crime working for Knightfall, another powerful adversary of Batgirl.

**An aspiring journalist** hoping to be the next Lois Lane, Lisly Bonner set her sights on a criminal, Boss Whittaker. When Whittaker found out she was wearing a voice recorder, he shot Lisly, and she plunged into the bay. The incident unlocked her mind-control powers, and she set out as the villain Gretel, intent on gaining control over the men that had made her powerless.

*"I envy that. I'm green all over."*

Rendered bald from her injuries, Gretel now wears different wigs to match her mood. She faced Batgirl with green hair, and Batman wearing blue hair.

# LORD DEATH MAN

## VITAL STATS

**Real Name:** Unknown

**Occupation:** Criminal

**Height:** 5ft 11in

**Weight:** 168 lbs

**Base:** Mobile

**Allies:** Leviathan, variety of henchmen

**Foes:** Rā's al Ghūl, Batman Japan, Batman, Dr. Darrk, Talon, the Outsiders

## POWERS AND ABILITIES

Able to die and come back to life; mentally unstable; superhuman durability and endurance; capable hand-to-hand combatant; utterly fearless due to his particular condition.

### SKELETONS IN THE CLOSET

After the fall of Leviathan, Rā's al Ghūl captured Lord Death Man in the hope of using the villain's death powers to his advantage. When Talon broke into one of al Ghūl's hideouts, he was forced to contend with the skeletal criminal.

**A former opponent of** Batman's, Lord Death Man reemerged recently in Japan when he killed the original Mr. Unknown. On a Batman, Inc. mission, Batman and Catwoman stopped Lord Death Man with the help of Jiro Osamu, Mr. Unknown's successor and the future Batman Japan. Unable to die, Lord Death Man has become a repeated thorn in Batman's side.

> **"Welcome to the Dead Heroes Club!"**

Lord Death Man rarely takes life-and-death situations seriously, despite having clashed with Talon, the Outsiders, and even Batman and Robin in the past.

# MARIONETTE

## VITAL STATS

**Real Name:** Unknown, called "Mali"
**Occupation:** Criminal
**Height:** 5ft 9in
**Weight:** 147 lbs
**Base:** Chicago
**Ally:** Dick Grayson
**Foes:** Johnny Spade, the Mad Hatter

## POWERS AND ABILITIES

Ability to mimic the movement and fighting techniques of others after witnessing them in action; extremely fit, fast, and agile; excellent hand-to-hand combatant.

## UNLIKELY ALLIES

Marionette is the Catwoman to Nightwing's Batman. Appearing to have a similar moral code, the two have worked together in the past. However, they still remain on opposite sides of the law.

**The young Mali** was once one of the Mad Hatter's favorite obsessions. Kidnapped into doing his mind-controlled bidding as his "Alice," she was shot by the Hatter. Cursed with a condition called "personality slipping," Mali relies on a rare drug, Kanium, to balance her mind. She does whatever she needs to, as Marionette, to keep a constant supply of the medicine.

The Mad Hatter's manipulation altered her mind

Unbalanced mind requires Kanium to function

Often steals to acquire Kanium

Skintight suit allows her range of movement

"This *one wants to pull our strings.*"

# TWEEDLEDEE AND TWEEDLEDUM

## VITAL STATS

**Real Names:** Deever and Dumfree Tweed

**Occupation:** Criminals

**Height:** Both 5ft 7in

**Weight:** Both 187 lbs

**Base:** Gotham City

**Ally:** The Mad Hatter

**Foes:** Batman, the Batman Family

## POWERS AND ABILITIES

Capable hand-to-hand combatants; very intelligent; proficient in a variety of weapons.

### DUMB AND DUMBER

More often than not, Tweedledee and Tweedledum serve as the insane villain Mad Hatter's hired muscle. Recently, they helped the Mad Hatter ransack homeless shelters in a frenzied search for the Hatter's delusional obsession, his lost "Alice."

Very intelligent, despite acting otherwise

Share almost identical traits

Dress to match their fictional namesakes

Capable fighters despite their size

**The Mad Hatter is not** the only villain to take his name from Lewis Carroll's book, *Through the Looking Glass*. When look-alike cousins, Deever and Dumfree Tweed, embarked on a life of crime, they adopted the identities of Tweedledee and Tweedledum. Having menaced Batman on their own, they have become allied with the Hatter.

*"Don't worry boss. We gonna—"*
*"—crush the little man."*

# HERETIC

ROGUE

## VITAL STATS

**Real Name:** None

**Occupation:** Terrorist

**Height:** 7ft 4in

**Weight:** 345 lbs

**Base:** Mobile

**Allies:** Talia al Ghūl, Leviathan

**Foes:** Batman, Robin, the Batman Family

## POWERS AND ABILITIES

Superhuman strength, endurance, and durability; weapons expert; master swordsman; excellent hand-to-hand combatant; seemingly unaffected by pain; wears protective armor that includes a jetpack to enable flight.

## BORN TO KILL

The Heretic was meant to be Robin's replacement, one Talia made sure Damian was aware of before she cast him out of her family. The Heretic trained in Yemen and killed many superhumans in preparation for his role as Talia's ally.

**Grown in a lab and** hatched out of a whale carcass by Talia al Ghūl and her clandestine Leviathan organization, the Heretic was a grotesquely aged "brother" to Talia's son, Damian Wayne—also known as Robin. Desperate to prove his love to Talia, the Heretic served her, destroying anyone who threatened Leviathan, including, eventually, Damian himself.

> *"I watch. I listen. I learn.*
> *I am Batman now."*

Underneath his robes, the Heretic wore Batman-styled armor. Despite his desire to please his mother, Talia hated the Heretic.

# LADY VIC

## VITAL STATS

**Real Name:** Lady Elaine Marsh-Morton

**Occupation:** Assassin

**Height:** 5ft 6in

**Weight:** 120 lbs

**Base:** England

**Ally:** Charlie Caligula

**Foes:** Batwing, Nightwing

## POWERS AND ABILITIES

Expert assassin, martial artist, hand-to-hand combatant, and sharp-shooter; prefers to use weapons that are old family heirlooms; well connected in the criminal underworld; quick, fit, agile, and cunning.

### LADY OF THE WORLD

Lady Vic seems at home in any environment, from the bright daytime streets of Mumbai, India, to the dark shadows of the Gotham City night. She is a professional, and usually does her job quickly and efficiently.

**Lady Vic's name is** short for "Lady Victim," but her actions point to her being more the predator than the prey. Hailing from a long line of British mercenaries, Lady Vic takes her job seriously. Recently, she nearly killed Batwing after taking on a mission to destroy any and all bat-themed vigilantes she encountered during her stay in Gotham City.

*"You're not the hero. You're a paycheck."*

When Lady Vic first met Batwing, she easily bested the hero, despite his armored suit of advanced technology.

# MERRYMAKER

## VITAL STATS

**Real Name:** Dr. Byron Merideth

**Occupation:** Criminal, former psychiatrist

**Height:** 6ft 1in

**Weight:** 194 lbs

**Base:** Gotham City

**Allies:** Harley Quinn, Mr. Freeze, Professor Pyg, Scarecrow

**Foes:** Batman, the Batman Family

## POWERS AND ABILITIES

Behavioral modification expert, willing to utilize extreme and controversial methods; master manipulator; highly intelligent; access to Arkham Asylum patients.

### IN LEAGUE WITH A MADMAN

The Merrymaker founded the League of Smiles, a gang devoted to the Joker. While he had no connection to the Clown Prince of Crime himself, he was more than willing to use the Joker's reputation for his own selfish gain.

**A psychiatrist at** Arkham Asylum, Dr. Byron Merideth was one of the doctors assigned to evaluate the Joker. He then started up a private psychiatric practice to exploit those influenced by the Joker. Adopting the persona of the masked Merrymaker, he convinced his Joker-obsessed patients to do his bidding as soldiers for the Joker's "grand crusade."

*"Merrymaker and the League of Smiles are just getting started."*

The Merrymaker aided Scarecrow and a few other Arkham inmates in creating a mass hallucination in Gotham City known as Gothtopia.

# MR. TOXIC

## VITAL STATS

**Real Name:** Hugh Marder
**Occupation:** Scientist, criminal
**Height:** 6ft 4in
**Weight:** 240 lbs
**Base:** Gotham City
**Allies:** The Penguin, Mr. Combustible, Imperceptible Man, Professor Radium
**Foes:** Batman, the Batman Family

## POWERS AND ABILITIES

Energy projection; excellent hand-to-hand combatant; genius-level intellect despite being mentally unbalanced; connections to Gotham City's criminal underworld.

### TOXIC TOUCH

Batman once battled Mr. Toxic in a laboratory inside Wayne Tower. The only way he could overcome Toxic's energy projections was by using a prototype energy deflector from his Utility Belt, developed by Lucius Fox.

**Working on a way** to travel forward in time, scientist Hugh Marder ran into problems. Wanting to cure his own genetic disease, Marder began creating clones of himself that eventually deteriorated. Unable to stop his disease, Marder adopted the protective suit of Professor Radium while his most stable clone became Mr. Toxic.

Mind unbalanced after faulty experiment

Projects crackling energy

Helmet has been shattered by Batman

*"I am no longer a carbon copy of you! I am your equal now, Marder!"*

# VORTEX

## VITAL STATS

**Real Name:** Unknown

**Occupation:** Criminal, former quantum physicist

**Height:** 6ft

**Weight:** 203 lbs

**Base:** Gotham City

**Allies:** Catwoman, Cheetah, Hellhound

**Foes:** Batman, the Batman Family, Killer Frost

## POWERS AND ABILITIES

Force-based powers allow him to repel anything near his person; athletic build; need for revenge against his enemies.

### BARS AND STRIPES

Vortex met Catwoman inside Arkham Asylum. To escape her cell, she convinced Vortex to stop taking his medicine and therefore activate his powers.

**Vortex started out** as a quantum physicist, working on an atom smasher. When he was sucked into the vortex of his own creation, he gained fantastic powers but lost some of his sanity. "Zebra man" found camaraderie among the criminal sect, and recently teamed up with Cheetah and several other animal-themed criminals including another Gotham City villain, Hellhound.

*"Now I'm awake and I got some scores to settle."*

Mentally unbalanced after accident

Force stripes cover entire body

Wears minimalistic costume

Powers can be held in check by medicine

# MR. COMBUSTIBLE

## VITAL STATS

**Real Name:** Unknown

**Occupation:** Criminal

**Height:** 6ft 3in

**Weight:** 199 lbs

**Base:** Gotham City

**Allies:** The Penguin, Mr. Toxic, Imperceptible Man, Hypnotic, Mr. Mosaic

**Foes:** Batman, the Batman Family, the Falcone Family

## POWERS AND ABILITIES

Seemingly made up of a mysterious chemical formula; can sense chemical compounds like explosives; very intelligent leader; many connections in the criminal underworld.

## A SHINING JEWEL

Mr. Combustible is highly resourceful and organized. This helped him rob several jewelry stores for Emperor Blackgate when a Man-Bat virus spread throughout Gotham City thanks to Blackgate's plotting.

**While Mr. Combustible's past** remains a mystery, he seems a perfect fit as a Gotham City crime lord, with his strange looks and aristocratic personality. Forced to work for the Penguin when he arrived in the city, Mr. Combustible has made the most of his situation by staying loyal to him, even during the brief time Emperor Blackgate took control of the Penguin's criminal empire.

> *"I'm sensing the presence of high explosives in this chamber!"*

During a recent battle between Arkham Asylum inmates and Blackgate prisoners, Mr. Combustible had his head shattered, but survived the encounter.

# VENTRILOQUIST

## VITAL STATS

**Real Name:** Shauna Belzer
**Occupation:** Criminal
**Height:** 5ft 11in
**Weight:** 115 lbs
**Base:** Gotham City
**Allies:** "Ferdie,"
the Secret Six
**Foes:** Batman, Batgirl,
the Riddler

## POWERS AND ABILITIES

Uses telekinetic abilities
to control the bodies
of others; connections
in the criminal
underworld; has a
dangerously disturbed
mind; manipulates
puppet to use as a
terrifying weapon.

## SHARP AS A SPLINTER

Shauna customized a puppet
she stole from a childhood
entertainer, placing drills
in his palms and treating
"Ferdie" as if he were alive.
She often uses Ferdie to
attack her victims.

Appears
sickly
and frail

Telekinetic ability
makes her a top
ventriloquist

Her puppet
brings out
her dark side

**Shauna Belzer was born** with a twin
brother who stole the limelight. While
Shauna was dubbed "Shabby Shauna"
by schoolmates, her brother became
a child star. Discovering she had
telekinetic abilities, she used them to
punish her teasing classmates, and her
twin brother. As an adult, she began
a criminal career as the Ventriloquist,
naming her puppet after her brother.

*"I don't like it when people
are rude, Ferdie."*

# WRATH

## VITAL STATS

**Real Name:** E.D. Caldwell
**Occupation:** CEO of Caldwell Technologies, criminal
**Height:** 6ft 2in
**Weight:** 210 lbs
**Base:** Gotham City
**Allies:** Emperor Blackgate, Scorn
**Foes:** Batman, Alfred Pennyworth, G.C.P.D.

## POWERS AND ABILITIES

Extremely intelligent; a wealthy businessman; access to cutting-edge weapons and vehicles; armored suit equipped with variety of weapons; expert martial artist and hand-to-hand combatant.

### DYSFUNCTIONAL DUO

Like Batman, Wrath considers himself a loner. But just as the Batman had adopted partners in the form of Robin and Batgirl, Wrath hired a cop killer in the form of Scorn. But when Scorn failed a mission, Wrath simply killed him.

Lenses enhance his vision

Highly armored suit

Shock gloves can dispense 60,000 watts of current

**The son of Mallory Caldwell,** a man killed by the G.C.P.D., E.D. Caldwell went on to found Caldwell Technologies, a weapons manufacturer. Wanting vengeance for his father's death, he made a bid to purchase Wayne Enterprises, but Bruce Wayne rejected his offer. Caldwell nonetheless launched an assault on the G.C.P.D., stopped only by Batman's interference.

*"...this is a game you're certain to lose."*

# VELVET TIGER

ROGUE

## VITAL STATS

**Real Name:** Lani Gilbert

**Occupation:** Criminal, CEO of GilCom

**Height:** 5ft 5in

**Weight:** 112 lbs

**Base:** Mobile

**Allies:** Stolen tigers

**Foes:** Batgirl, Batwing

## POWERS AND ABILITIES

Extremely fast and agile; has razor-sharp claws capable of cutting through cords easily; adept hand-to-hand combatant; computer expert; skilled in the use of knives.

### EARNING HER STRIPES

When Batgirl first faced Velvet Tiger, she was taken by surprise by the villain's prowess in a fight. Velvet Tiger turned the tables on Batgirl, injecting the Super Hero with her own tranquilizer dart.

**When a tiger attacked** the office building of Luke Fox's new startup, FoxTek, Batgirl got involved, fighting off a second tiger attack at a similar company. Batgirl discovered this was the handiwork of a new villain in Gotham City, Velvet Tiger. Realizing that this villain was Lani Gilbert, CEO of the failing tech company GilCom, Batgirl trailed Velvet Tiger, defeating her with the help of a remote-guided Batcycle.

*"Better to live one year as a tiger, than a hundred as a sheep."*

Velvet Tiger picked the wrong fight by kidnapping Jo, a friend of Batgirl's. Batgirl fought hard to defeat the villain's tigers, allowing Jo to escape.

# MORTICIAN

## VITAL STATS

**Real Name:** Porter Vito
**Occupation:** Criminal
**Height:** 6ft
**Weight:** 176 lbs
**Base:** Gotham City
**Allies:** The dead
**Foes:** Batman, the Batman Family

## POWERS AND ABILITIES

Brilliant chemist; developed a formula to bring dead bodies to life; obsessed with stopping death.

## WAKE THE DEAD

The Mortician was one of the many Batman villains who escaped Arkham Asylum during a recent breakout. He's not one to shy away from a good riot, and still holds a grudge against the Caped Crusader.

**After the death** of his parents, the Mortician became obsessed with bringing the dead back to life. A gifted chemist who had been criticized by his parents for indulging in the sciences, he battled Batman after one of the "zombies" he created committed murder. After Batman defeated the Mortician's army of the undead, the villain used a serum to put his parents to rest once more.

*"I often dream of killing him."*

The Mortician was one of the inmates Maggie Sawyer and Batwoman interviewed when Batwoman was trying to defeat the Dark Knight.

# TUSK

## VITAL STATS

**Real Name:** Unknown

**Occupation:** Gang boss

**Height:** 8ft 2in

**Weight:** 1,575 lbs

**Base:** Gotham City

**Allies:** His criminal lackeys

**Foes:** Dick Grayson, Batman, Robin

## POWERS AND ABILITIES

Superhuman strength and endurance; extremely tough skin that allows for enhanced durability; gang leader with many connections in the Gotham City underworld.

### DE-TUSKED

While Tusk gained the upper hand against Batman on their first encounter, the villain ultimately lost the fight thanks to Robin, who broke off one of the criminal's tusks. Later, Damian Wayne broke off the other tusk.

**Little is known about** Tusk's origins. Batman began to concentrate on the massive gangster's activities years ago, when Dick Grayson was out on his first official night of patrol as Robin. Although Batman fired Robin for not listening to his orders, Robin attacked Tusk, and managed to knock the villain from a helicopter, earning his place by Batman's side.

*"Time to pick on somebody my size."*

Why Tusk resembles an elephant remains a mystery, but what is known is that he has repeatedly returned to plague Dick Grayson.

# NOBODY

## VITAL STATS

**Real Name:** Morgan Ducard

**Occupation:** Mercenary

**Height:** 6ft 1in

**Weight:** 214 lbs

**Base:** Gotham City

**Allies:** Henri Ducard, NoBody II

**Foes:** Batman, Batman, Inc., Robin

## POWERS AND ABILITIES

Highly trained martial artist and assassin; hi-tech weaponized armored suit offers invisibility cloaking; enhanced vision; palm energy blasts; daughter currently wears similar suit with sonic upgrades.

## GHOST FROM THE PAST

Batman first became aware of NoBody's campaign against him when the villain killed the Batman, Inc. agent known as the Batman of Moscow. NoBody's desire for revenge was strong—he blamed Batman for disgracing him in front of his father.

Daughter wears similar suit after Morgan's death

**Special investigator** Henri Ducard trained his son Morgan in the ways of manhunting alongside Bruce Wayne —fostering a rivalry between Morgan and Bruce. Bruce later quit his training, and defeated Morgan as he tried to leave. Morgan returned as the villain NoBody, but was killed by Robin. His daughter, Maya Ducard, took on the role of NoBody.

Hi-tech invisibility capabilities

Armored suit protects from damage

> *"...You know I'll be back to kill you all..."*

# TIGER SHARK

## VITAL STATS

**Real Name:** Unknown
**Occupation:** Criminal
**Height:** 6ft 1in
**Weight:** 203 lbs
**Base:** Gotham City
**Allies:** Carmine Falcone, Bone
**Foes:** Dick Grayson, Batman, the Batman Family

## POWERS AND ABILITIES

Adept hand-to-hand combatant; excellent leader; has many ties in the criminal underworld; drawn to endangered animals; uses a cane as a weapon as well as firearms.

## THE FOOD CHAIN

When Carmine Falcone returned to Gotham City for a short period, Tiger Shark began working as his enforcer. Despite having an employer, Tiger Shark maintained a loyal entourage of lackeys who constantly spoke on his behalf.

**A modern day pirate** and smuggler, Tiger Shark made a major play to do business in Gotham City during the brief period when Dick Grayson took over for Bruce Wayne as Batman. Normally keeping just far enough off the coast of Gotham City to remain outside Coast Guard jurisdiction, Tiger Shark once used a gas pipeline to move material in and out of the city.

*"The tides will reclaim us."*

Mask made of seal skin

Hieroglyphics tattooed on tongue

Prefers clothing made from endangered species

# NOCTURNA

## VITAL STATS

**Real Name:** Natalia Mitternacht
**Occupation:** Criminal
**Height:** 5ft 10in
**Weight:** 140 lbs
**Base:** Gotham City
**Allies:** Night-Thief, Wolf Spider, Morgaine le Fey
**Foes:** Batwoman, Maggie Sawyer, Batman, Killshot, the Unknowns

## POWERS AND ABILITIES

Able to hypnotize others into believing a false reality or to be instantly smitten by her charms; connections to high society and the criminal world; adept at mind games.

### WICKED WITCH

Nocturna once fought Batwoman when the evil sorceress Morgaine le Fey altered reality to appear like something out of a fantasy novel. Nocturna worked directly for le Fey until the Unknowns restored the world to its natural state.

Capable hand-to-hand combatant

Very intelligent and a master planner

Skilled fighter who keeps in shape

**A former foe** of Batman's, Nocturna first crossed Batwoman's path when a villain named Wolf Spider broke her out of Arkham Asylum. She later used her hypnotic skills to be legally freed from the institution. Meeting Kate Kane (Batwoman) soon after, Nocturna came close to becoming a hero—until Batwoman discovered her crooked ways and defeated her.

*"Hello, Batwoman. Lovely to see you again."*

## VITAL STATS

**Real Name:** Unknown

**Occupation:** Criminal

**Height:** 6ft 4in

**Weight:** 240 lbs

**Base:** Gotham City

**Allies:** Scallop, Bootface, Smush, Bathead

**Foes:** Batman, the Batman Family

## POWERS AND ABILITIES

Employs a group of loyal lackeys who do his dirty work; vast stream of revenue enables purchase of warheads and technology to preserve his own life; armored battle suit provides enhanced strength and endurance.

## TERMINAL CASE

Terminus's rapidly deteriorating body required constant injections to sustain his life. He adopted a massive battle suit to fight Batman before his own death.

Battle suit armed with hi-tech weaponry

Body deteriorating at rapid pace

Technology helps to maintain life

**Terminus's origins** are mysterious. A villain whose body was literally falling apart, he knew the exact time of his upcoming death. Blaming Batman for his situation, he hired a team of criminals that had each been scarred by earlier encounters with Batman. They attacked Gotham City's citizens before Terminus unleashed a warhead —which was quickly defused by Batman.

*"...I wanted to see you die inside a little, right before I do."*

# PROFESSOR PYG

## VITAL STATS

**Real Name:** Lazlo Valentin

**Occupation:** Criminal

**Height:** 5ft 11in

**Weight:** 264 lbs

**Base:** Gotham City

**Allies:** Dr. Hurt,
Le Cirque d'etrange

**Foes:** Batman, Dick Grayson,
Robin, Carmine Falcone

## POWERS AND ABILITIES

Manic, unpredictable behavior; often aided by henchmen and an army of mind-altered Dollotrons; capable hand-to-hand combatant; considers murder and violence an art form.

### THIS LITTLE PIGGY WENT TO GOTHAM CITY

After his laboratory, located at Sinclair's Meats in Old Gotham, was burned down, Professor Pyg sought vengeance. He retaliated against his attacker, Carmine Falcone, deciding that all of Gotham City would now serve as his lab.

Recently employed animal-masked lackeys

Wears pig mask at all times

**When Batman first** encountered the villain calling himself Professor Pyg, it wasn't Bruce Wayne wearing the cape and cowl, it was Dick Grayson. In his brief stint as Batman, Grayson teamed with Robin to take down Pyg, a former low rent circus boss who decided to become an underworld criminal. The disturbed Pyg ran his operations from a deserted amusement park.

*"Pyg will make you perfect."*

# KGBEAST

## VITAL STATS

**Real Name:** Anatoli Knyazev

**Occupation:** Mercenary

**Height:** 6ft 3in

**Weight:** 231 lbs

**Base:** Russia

**Allies:** NKVDemon, Cheshire, Mayhem

**Foes:** Batman, Aquaman, the Others

## POWERS AND ABILITIES

Expert assassin, hand-to-hand combatant, and acrobat; superhuman strength, endurance, and durability; adept spy with strong connections in the intelligence and criminal worlds; weapons expert; fully stocked Utility Belt.

### MAKING MAYHEM

As a member of an organization called Mayhem, KGBeast teamed with several other heavyweight mercenaries, including his apprentice, the NKVDemon. Their plot to take over the world was foiled by the Others.

**An expert assassin,** KGBeast came to Gotham City years ago and clashed with Batman. Choosing to lose his own hand rather than admit defeat to the Dark Knight, KGBeast nevertheless ultimately failed in his mission. He continues to fight for Russia's "old ways," and recently fought with Aquaman and his team of allies called the Others.

Wears mask to hide his scarred face

Protective suit bears colors of the Soviet Union

Turned his severed hand into a weapon

*"We shall restore our country to what it once was..."*

## VITAL STATS

**Real Name:** Otis Flannegan

**Occupation:** Criminal

**Height:** 5ft 10in

**Weight:** 160 lbs

**Base:** Gotham City

**Allies:** Cluemaster, Menace, Firefly, Signalman, Lock-Up

**Foes:** Batman, Batwing, the Batman Family

### POWERS AND ABILITIES

Communicates with and controls rats; has connections to Gotham City's underground community and several above-ground criminals as well.

### RAT FINK

Severely mentally unbalanced, the Ratcatcher keeps a live rat in his helmet. He often has conversations with his rodents, and uses them to spy on people on Gotham City's streets, essentially giving him eyes and ears everywhere.

**A citizen of the underground**, the vast network of cities and towns below Gotham City, the Ratcatcher is obsessed with other residents of that dark world: rats. Working with the villain Menace, he used his command over rodents to help kidnap Batwing's sister, Tiffany Fox. He later joined forces with Cluemaster in an attempt to destroy Batman for good.

*"Heigh-ho the derry-o the cheese goes insane!"*

The Ratcatcher has trouble speaking. He prefers to communicate with his rodent allies rather than the crime bosses he's worked with.

# SUMO

## VITAL STATS

**Real Name:** Unknown
**Occupation:** Criminal
**Height:** 6ft 5in
**Weight:** 607 lbs
**Base:** Gotham City
**Allies:** The Squid,
Arkham Asylum inmates
**Foes:** Batman, Resurrection
Man, Bane

## POWERS AND ABILITIES

Extremely strong and
heavy; quicker than his
appearance implies; many
connections in the criminal
underworld; maintains
impressive endurance
and durability.

### SUMO WRESTLING

Batman first met Sumo when tracing
the source of a drug that killed Elena
Aguila, a friend of Bruce Wayne's. Inside
a shipping container, Batman activated
a pair of red glow sticks, only to find
himself facing Sumo's huge tiger tattoo.

**A familiar face behind the** bars
at Arkham Asylum, Sumo cuts an
intimidating figure in the criminal
underworld. Batman first encountered
the villain when he interrupted a
smuggling ring Sumo had been running
at Gotham City's docks. Batman
triumphed over the enormous villain,
learning that Sumo had worked with
a Gotham City crime boss, the Squid.

Mentally
unstable, he
enjoys violence

Wears scant
clothing and a
sumo's mawashi

Enormous body
can crush
opponents

*"I thought bats could
see in the dark!"*

# RED ALICE

## VITAL STATS

**Real Name:** Elizabeth Kane

**Occupation:** Vigilante, former criminal

**Height:** 5ft 11in

**Weight:** 141 lbs

**Base:** Mobile

**Allies:** Batwoman, the Unknowns

**Foes:** Mr. Bones, Morgaine le Fey, Nocturna

## POWERS AND ABILITIES

Skilled martial artist and gymnast; extensive understanding of military procedure; damaged mind from past trauma; adept hand-to-hand combatant; excellent marksman; wears protective suit equipped with variety of gadgets.

## ALICE DOESN'T LIVE HERE ANYMORE

Red Alice and Batwoman are sisters, but they couldn't be more different. Red Alice is constantly struggling with her sanity, often quoting lines from Lewis Carroll's *Through the Looking Glass* as her own speech.

**As a young girl,** Beth Kane was kidnapped alongside her twin sister, Kate Kane, and their mother. While their father, Jacob Kane, managed to rescue Kate, Beth was presumed dead, only to reemerge as the very disturbed super-villain Red Alice. Fighting her own sister who had adopted the identity of Batwoman, Red Alice was eventually defeated by her Super Hero twin.

*"Don't worry. I'm not here to kill you."*

After surviving her battle with Batwoman, Red Alice straightened out her life to become a vigilante on the right side of the law.

# THE SQUID

## VITAL STATS

**Real Name:** Lawrence Loman

**Occupation:** Criminal

**Height:** 5ft 6in

**Weight:** 173 lbs

**Base:** Gotham City

**Allies:** Sumo, Calendar Man

**Foes:** Batman, Harvey Bullock

## POWERS AND ABILITIES

Intelligent strategist and leader; many connections in the criminal underworld.

### TANKED
The Squid had no qualms about making an example out of someone who had wronged him. When his own brother's crew stole from him, the Squid dropped one of the men into the tank of a deadly giant squid.

Comfortable, lightweight jacket

No costume needed to exude an air of danger

Not afraid to get his own hands dirty

**The Squid was a** Gotham City crime boss who attracted Batman's attention after the death of Bruce Wayne's friend, Elena Aguila. Looking into Elena's death, Batman uncovered a network of criminals that included the Squid. Tracking him to an abandoned aquarium, Batman overcame the villain's pet squid before the Squid was killed by a rival criminal.

> *"...Gotham City is the monster that needs to be fed."*

# INDEX

Main entries are in **bold**.

## ARTIST ACKNOWLEDGMENTS

Christian Alamy, Juan Albarran, Oclair Albert, Rafael Albuquerque, Laura Alfred, Michael Alfred, Marlo Alquiza, Brad Anderson, Marc Andreyko, Joy Ang, Ulises Arreola, Mahmud Asrar, Michael Atiyeh, Tony Aviña, Matt Banning, Al Barrionuevo, Eddy Barrows, Jacob Bear, David Beaty, Tony Bedard, Ed Benes, Mariah Benes, Bengal, Ryan Benjamin, Marguerite Bennet, Joe Bennett, Rain Beredo, Lee Bermejo, W. Haden Blackman, Fernando Blanco, Blond, Roger Bonet, James Bonny, Brett Booth, Geraldo Borges, Andrei Bressan, Vera Brosgol, Jimmy Broxton, Brian Buccellato, Cullen Bunn, Riccardo Burchielli, Chris Burnham, Jim Calafiore, Greg Capullo, Juan Castro, Keith Champagne, Howard Chaykin, Clio Chiang, ChrisCross, June Chung, Vicente Cifuentes, Scott Clark, Andy Clarke, Ronan Cliquet, Becky Cloonan, Andre Coelho, David Cole, Simon Coleby, Amanda Conner, Will Conrad, Darwyn Cooke, Paul Cornell, Jorge Corona, Jeromy Cox, Wes Craig, Andrew Dalhouse, Federico Dallacchio, Tony S. Daniel, Marc Deering, Tom DeFalco, Werther Dell'Edera, Jesse Delperdang, Tom Derenick, Johnny Desjardins, Dan DiDio, Andy Diggle, Rachel Dodson, Terry Dodson, Jed Dougherty, Christian Duce, Dale Eaglesham, Scott Eaton, Gabe Eltaeb, Nathan Eyring, Jason Fabok, Nathan Fairbairn, Romulo Fajardo, Jr., Ray Fawkes, Raul Fernandez, Eber Ferreira, Julio Ferreira, Juan Ferreyra, Pascal Ferry, David Finch, Meredith Finch, Brenden Fletcher, Sandu Florea, Fabrizio Florentino, Jorge Fornes, Gary Frank, Derek Fridolfs, Richard Friend, Lee Garbett, Alex Garner, Javier Garrón, Sterling Gates, Dave Geraci, Drew Geraci, Ransom Getty, Sunny Gho, Keith Giffen, Jonathan Glapion, Adam Glass, Patrick Gleeson, Joel Gomez, Julius Gopez, Mick Gray, Justin Gray, Dan Green, Michael Green, Ig Guara, R.M. Guera, Andres Guinaldo, Scott Hanna, Chad Hardin, Joe Harris, James Harvey, Jeremy Haun, Rob Haynes, Doug Hazlewood, Daniel Henriques, Scott Hepburn, Meghan Hetrick, Hi-Fi Design, Kyle Higgins, David Hine, Bryan Hitch, Sandra Hope, Corin Howell, Adam Hughes, Ken Hunt, Rob Hunter, Gregg Hurwitz, Frazer Irving, Mark Irwin, Jack Jadson, Al Jaffee, Mikel Janín, Georges Jeanty, Paul Jenkins, Jorge Jimenez, Jock, Geoff Johns, Staz Johnson, Mike Johnson, Henrik Jonsson, Ruy José, Juancho, Dan Jurgens, John Kalisz, Jon Katz, Karl Kerschi, Karl Kesel, Tom King, Tyler Kirkham, Scott Kolins, Ales Kot, Andrew Kreisberg, Andy Kubert, Szymon Kudranski, Michel Lacombe, José Ladrönn, David Lafuente, Serge Lapointe, Ken Lashley, John Layman, Jae Lee, Jim Lee, Jay Leisten, Jeff Lemire, Rick Leonardi, Yishan Li, Rob Liefeld, LLC, Scott Lobdell, Jeph Loeb, Alvaro Lopez, David Lopez, Emilio Lopez, Aaron Lopresti, Lee Loughridge, Jorge Lucas, Ant Lucia, Emanuela Lupacchino, Doug Mahnke, Marcelo Maiolo, Guy Major, Alex Maleev, Francis Manapul, Leandro Manco, Clay Mann, Guillem March, Alitha Martinez, Allen Martinez, Alvaro Martinez, Christy Marx, José Marzan, Jr., Jason Masters, J.P. Mayer, Dave McCaig, Ray McCarthy, Trevor McCarthy, Scott McDaniel, Mike McKone, Lan Medina, Hermann Mejia, Javier Mena, Jaime Mendoza, Jesús Merino, Jonboy Meyers, Danny Miki, Romano Molenaar, Jorge Molina, Sula Moon, Stephen Mooney, Tomeu Morey, Moritat, Grant Morrison, Paul Mounts, Dustin Nguyen, Tom Nguyen, Fabian Nicieza, Ann Nocenti, Mike Norton, Kevin Nowlan, Sonia Oback, Patrick Olliffe, Guillermo Ortego, Andy Owens, Agustin Padilla, Greg Pak, Jimmy Palmiotti, Dan Panosian, Eduardo Pansica, Pete Pantazis, Yanick Paquette, Jeff Parker, Sean Parsons, Fernando Pasarin, Allen Passalaqua, Jason Pearson, Paul Pelletier, Pere Perez, Cris Peter, Will Pfeifer, Javier Piña, FCO Plascencia, Francis Portela, Howard Porter, Eric Powell, Joe Prado, Jack Purcell, Joe Quinones, Wil Quintana, Frank Quitely, Khary Randolph, Norm Rapmund, John Rauch, Sal Regla, Ivan Reis, Rod Reis, Cliff Richards, Tom Richmond, Jeremy Roberts, Roger Robinson, Kenneth Rocafort, Robson Rocha, Prentis Rollins, Alex Ross, Stéphane Roux, Felix Ruiz, Matt Ryan, Sean Ryan, Juan Jose Ryp, Jesús Saíz, Edgar Salazar, Tim Sale, Daniel Sampere, Rafa Sandoval, Derlis Santacruz, Trevor Scott, Tim Seeley, Emanuel Simeoni, Gail Simone, Alex Sinclair, Paulo Siqueira, Dan Slott, Brett Smith, Scott Snyder, Ben Sokolowski, Ryan Sook, Andrea Sorrentino, Chris Sotomayor, Peter Steigerwald, Cameron Stewart, Jeff Stokely, RC Stoodios, Karl Story, Carrie Strachan, Mico Suayan, Goran Sudzuka, Duane Swierczynski, Ardian Syaf, Phillip Tan, Babs Tarr, Jordi Tarragona, Ben Templesmith, Art Thibert, Frank Tieri, Marcus To, Peter Tomasi, Andy Troy, James Tynion IV, Ethan Van Sciver, Roberto Viacava, Dexter Vines, Alessandro Vitti, Joe Weems, Scott Williams, J.H. Williams III, Judd Winick, Ryan Winn, Marv Wolfman, Walden Wong, Jason Wright, Annie Wu, Matt Yackey, Craig Yeung, Richard Zajac, Patrick Zircher.

**SENIOR EDITOR** Victoria Taylor
**PROJECT EDITOR** Shari Last
**EDITOR** Laura Nickoll
**SENIOR DESIGNER** Robert Perry
**DESIGNERS** Chris Gould, Pallavi Kapur
**DTP DESIGNERS** Umesh Singh Rawat, Rajdeep Singh
**PRE-PRODUCTION PRODUCER** Siu Yin Chan
**PRE-PRODUCTION MANAGER** Sunil Sharma
**SENIOR PRODUCER** Alex Bell
**MANAGING EDITOR** Sadie Smith
**MANAGING ART EDITORS** Ron Stobbart, Neha Ahuja
**CREATIVE MANAGER** Sarah Harland
**ART DIRECTOR** Lisa Lanzarini
**PUBLISHER** Julie Ferris
**PUBLISHING DIRECTOR** Simon Beecroft
**ADDITIONAL DESIGN** Dynamo Limited

Dorling Kindersley would like to thank Josh Anderson and Amy Weingartner at Warner Bros. Global Publishing and Leah Tuttle at DC Entertainment. Thanks also to Julia March for the index, Joel Kempson, Lauren Nesworthy, Lisa Stock, and Chitra Subramanyam for editorial assistance, and Lisa Robb, Radhika Banerjee, and Ishita Chawla for design assistance.

This edition published in 2016
First American Edition, 2016
Published in the United States by DK Publishing
345 Hudson Street, New York, New York 10014
DK, a Division of Penguin Random House LLC

001-288722-Jan/2016
Page design Copyright © 2016 Dorling Kindersley Limited

A WORLD OF IDEAS:
**SEE ALL THERE IS TO KNOW**